Fightin' Oil

Fightin' Oil

BY

Claire

HAROLD L. ICKES

Petroleum Administrator for War

CHAPTER HEADING SKETCHES BY

CLARE B. METZGER

NEW YORK ALFRED A. KNOPF 1943

THIS BOOK HAS BEEN PRODUCED IN FULL COMPLI-
ANCE WITH ALL GOVERNMENT REGULATIONS FOR
THE CONSERVATION OF PAPER, METAL, AND OTHER
ESSENTIAL MATERIALS.

PUBLISHED JULY 6, 1943
SECOND PRINTING, AUGUST 1943
THIRD PRINTING, SEPTEMBER 1943

To RAYMOND WILMARTH,

ELIZABETH JANE,

and HAROLD McEWEN ICKES

A NOTE OF APPRECIATION

I wish to express my particular thanks to Geo. N. Briggs and Chandler Ide for their advice and help in the preparation of this book, and to pay tribute to all of the members of my staff who have worked so hard and loyally to make the extraordinary record upon which it is based.

THE AUTHOR

Foreword

When the President notified me by a letter dated May 28, 1941, that he had named me Petroleum Coordinator for National Defense (later changed to Petroleum Coordinator for War, and still more recently to the title at present in vogue — Petroleum *Administrator* for War, which entitles me to the paternal initials of *PAW*) the first thing that popped into my head was the definition that was then kicking about Washington: " A coordinator is a man who can tell you the time if you show him your watch."

I determined that within the terms of the appointment, I would prove that I could do more than read and write and tell time. I hadn't asked for the job, but since it had been given to me I was going to make a go of it.

The President had early recognized that nothing was more indispensable to defense — and to victory if war should come — than petroleum and its products. His letter of appointment went into detail as to how the office should function, but the essence of the assignment was contained in the following language: ". . . to make petroleum and petroleum products available, adequately and continuously, in the proper forms at the proper places . . . to satisfy military and civilian needs."

There were two ways in which I might have approached the job. I could have said to the President: " Mr. President, you have given me a bunch of tough hombres to deal with, and the only way that I can get along with them is for you to give me dictatorial power so that I can *tell* them what to do, and *see that they do it.*"

That would have been Hitler's way. In fact some people, including, I suspect, a good many oil men themselves, thought that it would be *my* way, too. But I fooled them. It just so happens that, in spite of contrary opinions here and there, I believe in the American system of free enterprise. It is also the fact that I believe that business can best do its part — in peace as in war — with the least possible direction, and with the least interference, by the Government. Besides, thought I, a 15 billion dollar industry such as petroleum is, ought to be big enough to get around without help from me or anyone else.

" Furthermore, Ickes," said I to myself, " here is an industry that is made up of a half a million men as thoroughly individualistic as any you will find on earth."

And I was asked to coordinate them!

The Story of Oil is one of the biggest and one of the most exciting in the library of business and war. I couldn't hope to tell it all within the limits of a small volume. One couldn't even tell the story of petroleum in peacetime in a much bigger book, to say nothing of petroleum in a war of all nations. Petroleum is a household word in many languages. It has helped to revolutionize our lives, and is on the way to bring about still greater changes. I don't flatter myself that I could take such a subject and offer more than a bare outline of it in the few pages that follow.

"*Fightin' Oil*" has a modest but, I think, an extremely important mission — to clear up a few issues that seem to have too many people confused, and at the same time to give a bird's eye view of the scope of oil's contribution to the winning of the war.

No one knows better than I do that much that is now appearing in print is bewildering and contradictory, and no one is more disturbed over this fact than I am, or than are the members of my staff. We have no control which enables us to limit discussions of oil to facts with a minimum of fiction. The most, I think, that we can do is to urge everybody to take seriously only statements from authorized sources, and to dismiss any other as hearsay.

The Petroleum Administration for War has access to all of the facts relating to petroleum production, distribution, and consumption — past, present, and well into the future. If the consumers of oil would be guided solely by the information and the advice originating from this Office, their minds would be easier, and so would our jobs.

The more nearly to achieve such an end this book is written. If the people will read it sympathetically they will get straighter on what the Battle of Oil is about, and, I believe, that clearer understanding will have a stimulating and a salutary effect on public thinking.

HAROLD L. ICKES

Petroleum Administrator for War

Washington, D. C.

Contents

Fightin' Oil

A BRIEF HISTORY OF HUMAN LOCOMOTION

From the Minneapolis Tribune

CHAPTER ONE

Oil's Mighty Job

The President would have been in great luck had he been able to choose for his Petroleum Administrator an Elijah — a worker of miracles — a major prophet who could peek into the future and tell what it held for the American people and their comrades-in-arms. I am in no irreverent mood when I suggest it. Nor have I ever been more serious.

It is recorded that Elijah of Tishbeh in Gilead made " a little oil in a cruse " sustain him and the widow woman of Zarephath and her son " and her house " for many days. We are not informed as to the size of the widow's household, nor are we told how many were " many days." We are left free to assume that quite a company of people was involved over a considerable period of time. The important point of the story is that the cruse of oil did not fail.

3

There was enough for everybody. It was on time. And it didn't dry up.

I lay no claim to being a deep student of the Bible, for all that I have read it many times — yes, once even from " kiver to kiver." For all that, I do not pretend that I am able to view Elijah's masterly handling of the widow's little oil problem with the eye of a connoisseur. By this one stroke of genius Elijah demonstrated that he would have been able to apply the principle of supply and distribution to this oil business of ours at a time when the very future of civilization depends upon having enough of it and getting it there before it is too late.

In other words, there is no doubt in my mind that if the widow woman of Zarephath had been completely out of oil, Elijah could have spoken the word and an ample supply of it would have appeared instantly from Gilead, or other distant point, in plenty of time to meet the widow's desperate need. Such a feat I would have considered even more noteworthy than the one of making " a little oil in a cruse " sustain the prophet, the widow, her son, and her house for many days.

In the spirit of Elijah, the American people are today making their cruse of oil sustain them and their fighting sons and their allies, and they will continue to do so for as many days as it may take to drive Hitler and all of his works from off of the face of the earth. The real challenge is to deliver oil of specified grades, in sufficient quantities, over stretches of land and sea that vary in length from 3,000 to 10,000 miles, and to deliver it on time to do the job, the doing of which depends upon oil, and ever more oil, up to our capacity to supply, refine, and transport it.

Would Herr Hitler give an Elijah who could solve the Nazi oil problem a quitclaim deed to half of his kingdom? I think that he would.

We could ourselves afford to make such a person a very liberal offer.

There being no Elijah available, however, the American people must place their trust in the petroleum industry, which ought to be easy for those who are impressed by big figures. Before the war the United States petroleum industry had a gross investment of nearly 15 billion dollars; it employed directly 1 million people with an estimated annual payroll of 1 and a half billion dollars. It was spending another billion dollars a year for services and supplies, thus providing employment for an additional 200,000 workers. Petroleum and its by-products represented 40 per cent of the total mineral production of the country.

Although these figures may not be truly typical of the industry under the present chaotic world conditions, they should encourage us to believe that the job is at least in the most capable hands. And there is additional comfort in the fact that the American petroleum industry has placed at the disposal of its country all of the benefits of its chemical research in which it has spent, according to some estimates, another 4 billion dollars.

Speaking before the Petroleum Industry War Council at Washington a few weeks ago, Mr. Geoffrey Lloyd, M.P., Chairman of the British Oil Control Board, and

Great Britain's Petroleum Secretary, made this statement:

"I don't have to tell you how important is gasoline. That would be an anticlimax. But I would like to relate to you a bouquet to the American oil industry from what I think to be an unexpected quarter.

"One of my representatives was present at the banquet when Prime Minister Churchill was entertained by Premier Stalin, and after the dinner was over Premier Stalin rose and held his glass of Russian champagne and said:

"'This is a war of engines and octanes. I drink to the American auto industry and the American oil industry.'

"Premier Stalin is a realist, and he was telling the truth. I would like you to know Premier Stalin's estimate of the importance of oil to the success of this war."

It becomes more evident, as distances are annihilated, that this organized human slaughter in which the world is now engaged, is moving to a tempo that petroleum may, in a sense, be said to have set. Had there been no such thing as oil, I doubt if there would have been a global war. Without oil, I don't see how we could now be fighting on all sides of the earth. It is possible that nature would have given us something else to fight with. Hitler, naturally, expected to "blitz" his way to world power from the sky. He was thinking of himself as the "reincarnation" of the great god Wotan. But without petroleum the idea would scarcely have presented itself even to a mad Austrian paperhanger.

We may at least be sure that, without oil, this war

would not have been fought on its present grand scale. The spectacular hit-and-run attacks which our fliers are staging every day over many wide fronts — the reminder to the Japs that their beloved Tokyo is not beyond our reach even if their ancestors and their sun goddesses are on guard — would have been impossible but for petroleum. An oilless war, had there been a war, would have been pretty dull business compared with the well-lubricated maneuverings of millions of men, not only on the ground, but on the surface of the waters, in the air, and under the seas. If, therefore, oil has set the pace of this war, oil must see it through, and the side that can throw the most oil into the fray over the longest sustained period of time will win.

I may as well confess at the outset that many times I have wished, with all of the fervency of prayer, for the spiritual power of a major prophet. There is no denying that there have been blue Mondays when I have wondered if our production and transportation of petroleum could possibly keep pace with the growing military and essential civilian needs. If it does, let me say right here, without fear of successful contradiction, that we will have been a witness to a miracle worthy of the saints of old.

It will, in other words, be little short of a metaphysical achievement to fuel the 185,000 American bombers and fighting planes that we expect to have in the air before "finis" is written to the war; the 18 million tons of merchant ships that we have been promising ourselves; the 120,000 tanks that will one day soon be blazing away at the enemy; not to mention the hundreds of thousands of trucks and other vehicles that carry supplies to the front. Without oil, every piece would be just so much scrap metal — and no more. Having fueled and lubricated these gasoline and oil eaters of land and air, we will have only started the job. We will still have our Navy to supply; we will still have to keep our allies stocked so that their bombers and tanks and mobile artillery may be kept moving; we will still have to feed the automobile tanks of our defense workers and, within reason, meet the essential needs of our civilian populations; and we will still have to pour oil into the thousands of war industries working three shifts a day, and into the millions of homes and buildings that have no substitute for oil heat.

Every one of the thousands of bombers that are taking off daily for a go at the enemy must carry enough gasoline for the trip home, so that when we speak of a flying radius of 1,000 miles we are speaking in terms of a gasoline volume never before thought possible of achievement. We are going to see bigger and ever-bigger air fleets, made up of ever-larger planes, capable of negotiating longer and ever-lengthening distances, and for these myriad giants of the air we must brew a particular type of gasoline which, until a few years ago, had been only a laboratory curiosity. In addition to this specialized gasoline for the fliers, plus unlimited quantities of high-quality gasoline for our tanks and trucks, and fuel oil for the Navy, together with high-grade lubricants for virtually every use abroad and at home, we must produce prodigious amounts of toluene for quantity production of explosives, and butadiene for the manufacture of synthetic rubber.

It has been reliably estimated that about 60 per cent, or nearly two out of every three tons of the supplies sent overseas to our expeditionary forces are oil.

Under Secretary of War Robert P. Patterson has made the startling statement that the gasoline supply for the military services in North Africa is "on the basis of a planned requirement of *10 gallons per day per vehicle. . . .*" Now there are literally hundreds of thousands of supply trucks and armored vehicles belonging to the Allied nations that are drawing on the United States for the major portion of their fuel supply. Multiply the number by ten and you may get a faint notion of the petroleum that is needed every day to keep our army rolling.

We have the word of British officials that a battleship, on a short cruise, will consume in the neighborhood of a million gallons of oil, and that the consumption by the British Navy is measured by tens of millions of gallons a week. What is true of England's navy is equally true of our own.

Does anyone know of a word, or of a combination of words, that adequately describes the size of the job and the responsibility that faces petroleum in this fight? If he does, I would like to have it to add to my vocabulary because I, for one, am hopelessly lost for language to express them.

But for all its enormity the job is going to be done simply because it has to be done — and a better reason than that I wouldn't be able to give.

One of the most distinguishing differences between Hitler's plight and our own problem is that whereas we have much more crude in the ground to start with than Germany possesses or controls — and are confronted with the pressing problems of home consumption, transportation to the far-away battle fronts, and wide and wise distribution the world over — Hitler, in addition to having the same difficulties in varying degrees, must conquer some unconquerable people before he can hope to add substantial stocks to his limited supply of natural crude. Of course the Germans can make quantities of synthetic gasoline within the inelastic compass of their manpower and critical materials. If we have to come to it, we, too, can make synthetic gasoline out of our abundant coal and shale deposits. But while we praise the Lord and continue to pump oil, let us also resign ourselves to the near certainty that we will never win this war merely because the petroleum supplies of the enemy have dried up.

Here may be as good a place as any to face squarely a set of realities. We have long comforted ourselves with the belief that the United States has an unlimited supply of petroleum — that we would never be caught short. This is a misconception that should not be used as a basis for any far-reaching conclusions. Our supply is *not* inexhaustible, as I shall later attempt to explain. Our proven reserves compare favorably with those of other countries — Russia, for instance, the Near East,

the South American oil countries, Mexico, and others
— but we should not permit ourselves to be blown up
over what we think our relative position in the world
of oil is, because in the matter of potential resources
our position is not nearly so favorable. As I shall have
occasion to emphasize, we are burning oil faster than
we are producing it, and new discoveries are not keeping pace with production.

Oil is nothing new in the world, even if its discovery
came later than some other things. If its uses were slow
in being recognized, they have literally been multiply-
ing like rabbits now that man has really begun to find
and develop its potentialities. Oil's wider and more
diversified possibilities have been forced into the open
by world affairs, and mere man — not being an Elijah
— is having his hands full producing and harnessing
enough of the precious stuff to do a million and one
jobs, both old and new, each job important of itself,
and some of them more important than anything else.

Since the Nazis and the Japanazis started on the
rampage, the world of science and invention has accomplished what normally it would have taken 50
years to do. This is especially true of the American
petroleum industry. Since they found themselves face
to face with the job of furnishing power to the biggest
part of a world under arms, American oil men have
been moving in the stratospheric reaches, and I appre-
hend that when Hitler and Tojo and Mussolini are at
last tied up they will be ready to admit with the poet
that " even the gods cannot strive against necessity."
No doubt they will be meditating at the time with

gloomy particularity upon the American petroleum industry, which, with the biggest order of its life to fill, went to work with grim determination and became, as much as any other single factor, responsible for the means by which the war is being fought, and by which it will be won eventually by the United Nations.

When I assert that the petroleum industry is entitled to high honors, I do so with a grateful acknowledgment of what other industries are contributing to the result. But without oil — enough of it, I mean, — metals, rubber, bombs, ships, tanks, airplanes, everything that will be needed in great abundance to win the war and purge civilization of the Hitlers and the Hirohitos and the Quislings — would be either useless or of far less effectiveness.

It is an extremely difficult undertaking to discuss a subject which is necessarily so closely guarded by the censorship as petroleum at war. The enemy is striving daily by every means to discover our true and improving circumstances. And there are Lavals within who would jump at a chance to sell us out on a matter so vital to ultimate victory as is petroleum.

We know, for instance, how characteristically and industriously the Japs worked before Pearl Harbor to uncover the facts concerning our petroleum supply and its whereabouts. Can there be any doubt that they were preparing for the day when Amaterasu, their favorite sun goddess, would guide them through the air with the greatest of ease to drop bombs on our oil tanks?

(I am thinking at the moment of a particular letter that was written as far back as June 25, 1940, on the letterhead of the Mitsubishi Company, Japanese importers (full name, Mitsubishi Shoji Kaisha, Ltd., head office Tokyo), and addressed to the editor of one of the leading American petroleum journals. It is clear evidence to me that the Japs had formed a pretty low opinion of our credulity.

The letter in question originated in the San Francisco office of the Mitsubishi Company. The writer requested several pieces of vital information, (1) " name of companies who have alkylation and/or isooctane plants in California, its capacity (each) and date of construction," and (2) " by whom and how many are in process of being constructed, when will it be completed and its capacities.")

With characteristic tail-wagging, the writer expressed his " honorable admiration " for the research value of the magazine, and ended on a note of impatience that the data be collected as quickly as possible. It was suggested that " even an estimate of the capacity for the above will be appreciated." (I have since seen the name of the Mitsubishi Company mentioned in published reports of FBI investigations of subversive activities.)

There is some satisfaction to be had from the knowledge that the editor did not furnish the information. For one reason, he said, it wasn't to be had. I like to think that he wouldn't have given it out for other reasons, the most important of which would have been that by June of 1940, when the letter was written, we should have been privy to the fact that the Japs were up to no good and were even then plotting our downfall.

I am reminded of another painful occasion when, for the mere asking, the Japanese Government was permitted to purchase a gigantic relief map of the San Francisco Bay area showing in scrupulous detail the locations, the kinds of, and the distances between the industrial plants and oil refineries of that section. The map had been on exhibition at the San Francisco Exposition and, therefore, everybody, including the Japs, had had plenty of opportunity to study it. But the Japs are a painstaking race, and here was an opportunity to acquire a key map (cost no object) on the sniveling pretext that they "admired" it so much that they wished to own it as an unusually fine specimen of mapmaking! Not to be outdone in politeness, someone sold the map, apparently without a single question, to the Nipponese! What useful Japanese purpose the map has served I do not know, but the transaction indicates how cuddly we were right up to the eve of Pearl Harbor.

(As far back as 1923 an American petroleum engineer paid a visit to the Island of Sakhalin, the whole of which was at that time occupied by the Japanese. His purpose was "just to look about." He was promptly slapped into jail where he was allowed to languish for a few weeks before the Japs blindfolded him, whirled him around a few hundred times, and started him for home. That's what the Japs do to people who ask questions.)

And may this be a lesson to us! Let us resolve that from this time forth, whether in peace or in war, we, too, will hear nothing, know nothing (for publication), see nothing, say nothing. If this resolution should be kept in time of peace, the war will have brought us more than victory.

If I stray momentarily from the subject that I started out with, my excuse is that as oil is our most vital fluid asset, it is consequently the subject of more military and civilian conversation than almost any other factor outside of manpower itself. And in our discussions of it we should keep especially close guard over our tongues.

Even in World War I petroleum was described by Georges Clemenceau to be " as necessary as blood."

What the great French leader thought of petroleum a quarter of a century ago was recently stated in other language by a horny-handed oil driller from New Mexico:

" Being an oil driller since the last war hasn't blinded me to the fact that this war is going to be won with five essential things: guts, steel, oil, groceries, and a lot of faith."

The oil driller put oil where it belongs — in exclusive company. The householder who moves up his thermostat, or doesn't convert to coal when he could do so as well as not, and the driver who skims along the highway on a useless mission at a speed in excess of the limit, should keep these two estimates of oil ever before him.

Many of us recall the experience of the last war. Frequently it is alluded to in connection with the present in terms of petroleum production and consumption, but on examination it must be admitted that the last war was no more than an introduction to the real thing.

In published proceedings of the Naval Institute, November 1924, Captain Paul Foley of the U. S. Navy cites the forecast of the total requirements of petroleum over the last six months of 1918 as 4,587,524 tons. Of this total about 80 per cent was supplied by the United States. Reduced roughly to barrels, this represents a total petroleum requirement for *all* of the allies of less than 180,000 barrels per day. I cannot make public the comparable figures as to the demands of the armed forces today, but the consumption of any one single product is several times the *total* petroleum requirement in the last war. Crude oil production in the United States in 1918 was 975,000 barrels per day. Today it is more than 4,000,000 barrels per day.* It may well be said, therefore, that today we are face to face with a job that is without parallel.

How well prepared are we to do this job?

Have we the organization, the facilities, and the basic resources adequate for the purpose?

---

* An even more striking comparison of the first and the present world wars is contained in the statement found in Max W. Ball's book " This Fascinating Oil Business," that the equipment of a typical division in World War I had a horse power of 4,000, whereas a present-day mechanized division requires about 187,000 horse power.

Have we sufficiently well-defined and well-coordinated plans of operation?

Does the industry know what is expected of it?

Finally, what of the spirit — the will to do — which animates and propels?

As one well-known American used to suggest — " let's look at the record."

CHAPTER TWO

Enough Oil
and On Time

We promise you that if it is humanly possible, we will get oil to our fighters on all fronts, at whatever cost, and at whatever sacrifices at home.

Paste that in your hat, and the next time you feel like pillorying the Petroleum Administrator, remove it and read the promise that he has made here. It is a promise to our fighting forces.

So long as men are willing to stake their lives on the chance of piloting petroleum safely through sub-infested waters, then the least that we at home can do is to see that the stuff so desperately needed by our boys abroad doesn't miss the boat.

The only language that Hitler and his hordes will ever understand is that of bullets and bombs, and more bombs; the only ones who can speak fluently and convincingly in their tongue are the boys behind the guns;

18

the only way that they have of getting close enough for Hitler to hear what they are saying is by tank or plane or truck filled with the gasoline and the oil that only Uncle Sam is able to furnish in sufficient quantity. And the only way that Uncle Sam has of getting enough petroleum supplies into their hands to achieve this end is by filling and shipping the tankers that normally serve the East Coast and the Pacific Northwest areas.

Despite an unbelievable accomplishment in developing substitute transportation for oil — about which more is to be said — we have still been unable to move enough oil overland to meet all needs. That is why stern measures have been necessary to hold down civilian consumption. And that is why I have spent so much time during the past three years in the public doghouse.

What we at home can do to help the most in bringing this war to a successful climax is to train and arm the men and give them the means — machines and petroleum — with which to wipe out Hitler and all that he represents. Fully as important as manpower and guns and machines is the fuel that makes it possible for the men to drive the machines across land and sea and through the air in hot pursuit of everything on two legs that bears even a slight resemblance to a Hitlerat.

The story of gasoline and fuel oil in this country is one of the most dramatic and colorful in our business history. In its relation to the war and our home life it has been discussed in all of its many cadences over the air, in type, and through loud speakers. It has been digested at every American dinner table. It has been rehashed at every filling station, garage, and corner store. Notwithstanding all of that, it continues to be a prime topic of animated conversation, and subject matter for " galluppolls."

Occasionally I regret that I am required to spend so much of my war effort reiterating the fundamental proposition that a gallon of oil saved, i.e., not burned in the oil heater or in the automobile cylinder, is fuel for the fire which the United Nations are kindling under the despicable Nazis. But so far as the total petroleum problem is concerned, it never loses its grip on my interest, and I only hope that I may be able to impress some of that which I consider to be its spectacular appeal upon the reader of this book.

Every so often I am likened to Cassandra, that lady of Greek legend who so displeased the gods that they decreed that she would always have the right answers, but that no one would ever believe them. Cassandra and I would undoubtedly have hit it off splendidly considering the fact that, up to a few months ago, very few would believe me either. For at least a year I was the only one, outside of a few intimates, who took my misgivings seriously.

The last time that I saw Paris, nearly five years ago, I was convinced that a world war was in the making. This opinion did not spring full grown from my teeming brain; it was the summation of the views which I had had from competent analysts on the ground, plus my personal observations. It took considerably less

The bed is nearly ready for " Big Inch " and its river of oil.

"Big Inch" rolls over the hills of Missouri.

than a crystal ball to foresee that if a global war did come it would be fought principally with petroleum. The next logical conclusion was that, although the United States was fortunately situated with respect to petroleum, the kind of a war that was obviously hatching in the tortured minds of the German leaders would put a great strain even upon our seemingly unlimited resources.

Gradually, piece by piece, as a jigsaw puzzle is put together, I formed a mental vision of the future that augured none too well for world peace. I take no particular credit unto myself for having seen somewhat ahead and distinguished the outline of trouble. I had been given an opportunity soon after my arrival in Washington in 1933 to obtain intimate, official, and first-hand knowledge of our petroleum supplies and of the petroleum industry itself. This information, and the increasing smell of smoldering powder over Europe, forced an opinion upon me that I could not prevail upon many others to share.

With my usual hangdog reticence when I am worried by public affairs I began to air my fears. Perhaps I would have been better off personally to have let nature take its course. All that I did for the time being was to bring down upon my head the maledictions and anathemas of the millions of people who wouldn't agree with me because they didn't want to, and the thousands of newspapers that thought it a heaven-sent opportunity to bump off an enemy of long standing. But having gone out on the limb, I saw nothing to be gained by crawling back, especially since the longer

I remained out there looking about me the more
certain I became that I wasn't just seeing spots.

I suggested timidly, as is my wont, that to play safe
we ought to build a few pipe lines, or at least *a* pipe
line if that were the best that we could do, from deep
in the heart of Texas, where most of our oil flows, to
the Eastern Seaboard. But apparently the country
wasn't ready for it.

That was in the summer of 1940. When, a year
later, Great Britain borrowed 50 oil tankers from us,
I made my suggestion for pipe lines in a much louder
voice because by that time it had become my responsibility by order of the President to see to it that, if
possible, there would be no diminution in the quantity of petroleum supplies shipped to the Atlantic
Coast area. It was evident to us that gasoline and fuel
oil users of that section would be the first to feel the
pinch. But again I was sat upon hard as a dreamer of
pipe dreams — a warmonger who was insisting crazily
that we were going to have trouble delivering all of
the oil that everybody wanted or thought that they
needed. Steel for pipe lines was denied on three occasions; strong lobbies worked in State legislatures and
in the National capitol to defeat efforts to acquire
rights-of-way by condemnation just in case any one
should be lucky enough to get his hands on critical
materials and start laying pipe lines.

Our coastwise shipping of petroleum dropped off
sharply, and I was all but burned in effigy for agreeing
to the diverting of tankers to England when England,
according to the back-seat coordinators, really didn't

want or need them. Then there was the matter of approximately 90,000,000 barrels of oil that we had been importing yearly to the East and Gulf Coasts from Mexico and South America which began at that stage to fade away. Our uncertain imports today will probably average not more than 8,000 barrels a day, or between 2,000,000 and 3,000,000 barrels a year.

To make matters worse — for me — Great Britain one day returned most of the tankers that she had borrowed, and then my critics became more than ever voluble and convinced that my I.Q. was somewhere in the scholastic neighborhood of McGuffey's Third Reader. I have never attempted to publicize the sequel, but the fact is that not many months later England asked to have all of the tankers sent back, plus as many more as we could spare. These have been in the war service ever since.

Whatever the popular — or unpopular — opinion of me and the tanker episode was back in 1941, the indisputable fact is that the underlying, basic cause of our oil problem stems from the withdrawal for military service of tankers which normally supplied the East Coast and the Pacific Northwest areas. From peacetime pursuits, tankers were drafted for the more grisly business of war. Many of them were sunk. Sinkings continue today. Tankers provide the petroleum life line to our troops and to our allies. They are the means, as well, of furnishing oil to Canada and to certain of the South and Central American countries whose industries are essential to the war program.

There has been so much uninformed discussion of

the railroad tank car situation that a revelation of the facts should make for a clearer understanding of the difficulties which faced us in those early days of the emergency.

With the disruption of the tanker service, the first natural alternative to suggest itself to the public mind was the railroad tank car. Not to overlook anything, I dusted off my old plans and renewed my agitation for pipe lines, realizing, of course, that even if we were given the " go " sign, it would be a year at least before they would be in service. But we didn't get the " go " sign even then. We had it dinned into us instead that there were thousands upon thousands of idle railroad tank cars rusting on every siding in the country. I doubted it but was more than willing to be shown.

Congress was told that unused equipment was lit-erally jamming the country, and that if the Petroleum Coordinator for National Defense (that was my title in those days) wasn't so cussed blind that he wouldn't see, the emergency could be met quickly, tankers or no tankers. Newspapers reproduced photographs of long lines of tank cars apparently standing and doing nothing in railroad yards, and in the captions I was invariably chided for rank pig-headed inefficiency in not putting them to work. No mention was made of the fact that in most all cases they were already work-ing, and that when the photographs were taken the cars were in the process of being unloaded and turned around for another trip.

For all of the great hullabaloo that was raised, in and out of Congress, about how much oil could be hauled in the idle tank cars of the country, the situation did not improve and the outlook for petroleum on the Atlantic Seaboard darkened. Although our surveys showed that there was no surplus of idle tank cars worth mentioning, we surmised that the best way to bring them out of hiding, if that's where they were, was to have the oil companies place orders for them.

It may not be known generally that oil companies own relatively few tank cars. Most of them are owned by companies that build and lease them. A comparative few are owned by the railroads that use them to haul their own fuel oil and other products.

The oil companies meanwhile had been trying to meet the tanker loss by building up a tank car movement to the East Coast which, compared to normal times, was fairly substantial. It was our conviction, however, that no great number of additional cars would be obtained if we were to rely on *idle* equipment, so we tackled the herculean job of *making* cars available for the East Coast run through withdrawals from actual service elsewhere in the country. This, of course, necessitated drastic changes in normal oil transportation methods on a nation-wide basis, and it took time. And while proceeding to do just this, we did not overlook any other possibility, however remote we might believe it to be.

We invited the heads of the biggest oil companies in the country to meet with us in Washington, and there the grim facts were laid before them. The East Coast faced a serious oil famine that threatened to paralyze war industries, tie up transportation, and result in great hardship from cold. We were not yet in the war, but in one of the finest exhibitions of patriotism and good faith that I have ever witnessed, these men — eleven of them — came to an agreement and set their hands to a remarkable document * in which it was agreed that " each company will immediately ask for and utilize in petroleum transportation all the available railroad tank cars it can obtain to the extent that its storage, car loading, other facilities and requirements will permit until shortage conditions are terminated."

This was, in effect, a blank check involving a potential expenditure of hundreds of millions of dollars.

We could make the oil industry heads no promise that the Government would help them carry the load, but we did express a willingness to recommend lower freight rates and to support, with the Office of Price Administration, the companies' application for an equitable price adjustment to take care of the additional costs of transportation which resulted from the insistence by the Government that more and more petroleum products be transported to the Eastern States by tank car. (It is only fair to record here that it was nearly a year before the added costs which had been piled upon the oil companies were absorbed.)

Telegraphic orders for railroad tank cars were immediately placed, some of the companies asking for as many as a thousand cars at a time. One company was able to get fifty. Another lured three out of hiding. One company head wired to 76 tank-car companies,

---

* See Appendix.

expressing a need for 1,000 more cars. Of the 76, answers were received from 64 offering a grand total of 160 cars out of 125,337 owned and in service. And so it went. By this simple and practical expedient it was established beyond a shadow of a doubt that the 20,000 " idle " railroad tank cars that the country had been hearing so much about were myths and did not exist, and that if we were to maintain anywhere near a normal movement of oil to the East Coast, we would have to resort to other and more arbitrary practices.

It became necessary to locate and draft cars that were in other services in sections of the country that were better situated with respect to gasoline and heating oil supplies than the Atlantic Coast States, or which could be served as well by other means of transportation. By a series of radical readjustments, such as the elimination of cross hauls and back hauls, the substitution of motor trucks for the shorter hauls out of refineries and bulk plants, the prohibition of unessential gasoline movements by tank cars, and the maximum possible substitution of barges and pipe lines, tank cars were freed in ever-increasing numbers until more than 70,000 of them are now delivering oil to our eastern terminals where formerly there was virtually no movement of oil by the railroads. (Numbered among the 70,000 cars are 700 that had been transporting wine! I am as fond of wine as the next person but I also like to keep warm!)

Obviously we could have had no benefit even if we had had all of the tank cars in the world if there hadn't been an experienced and efficient organization at hand to take them over and haul them once they were available for service. To add thousands of tank cars to the normal movement of freight and to keep them moving with maximum efficiency through congested terminals and, some of the time, over single-track railroads, was a monumental job of dispatching for which I give the railroads grateful credit.

One example of it is worth reciting. Freight trains that included a few tank cars were once made up in such a way that literally days were spent in switching and dropping off a car here and a car there. Today solid trains of oil cars are running on fast, uninterrupted schedules from oil fields and refineries to the eastern terminals. Tank cars built to run 20 miles an hour are now carried along at the rate of 40 miles an hour. This logically has necessitated a material increase in repair crews if the equipment is not to be permitted to wear out before its time. Turn around times over identical routes have been cut down and the solid trains of " empties " return for more oil on the same fast, uninterrupted schedules. The average round trip from Texas to the East is from eighteen to twenty days and from the nearby Midwest, about eleven days, which means that between 3,500 and 4,000 cars have been unloaded daily in the eastern terminals while the rest of the 70,000 cars have been traveling.

An orchid, too, to the Office of Defense Transportation for the good job that it perforce had to do in cooperation with the railroads and the Petroleum

Administration if the program were to succeed as well as it has.

With the recent opening of the War Emergency Pipe Line to Norris City, Illinois, from Longview, Texas, many of the tank cars were put on the shorter run from Norris City, where, instead of in Texas, they were assigned to pick up their loads and deliver them to the East which they are doing in approximately half of the time formerly consumed. This has materially increased the volume of oil delivered every 24 hours to the Atlantic Seaboard. But, of pipe lines, more later.

To handle the large volume of oil arriving by tank car that was once brought in by tanker, it has been necessary for the oil companies to construct new loading and unloading racks. Solid train shipments have necessitated the joint operation of terminal facilities to achieve the highest efficiency, and to this series of readjustments was later added the movement of box cars containing drums of petroleum which has already reached a peak of about 25,000 barrels per day. It is not expected, however, that the box car movement will be a permanent addition to the petroleum transportation system.

There were, let me repeat, no " idle " railroad tank cars to speak of with which to meet the emergency created in 1941 by the diversion of tankers to war duty. The " treasure hunt " undertaken by the oil companies in cooperation with the Government brought into service in the East the present total of

more than 70,000 tank cars. In the custody of the
railroads and with the cooperation of the ODT these
70,000 tank cars had been speeded up and systematized
until today when we are shooting at the amazing delivery total of a million barrels of oil in one day. (A
new record of 962,000 barrels daily of petroleum products moved by tank car to the East Coast was established as of May 1.) To put it another way, since the
beginning of the emergency, to date, we have multi-
plied by more than 150 times the amount of oil moved
by railroad tank car into the Eastern States. But we are
still not satisfied and are expecting the railroads to
show further improvement through increased efficiency, shorter hauls, etc.

My hat is off to the oil companies and to the railroads for the spirit and the skill with which they
have met and are rapidly overcoming what once appeared to be not only endless but unsurmountable
difficulties.

The more than 70,000 tank cars that have gone to
war in the East Coast service constitute, however, only
one link of this gigantic shipping chain which will ultimately wrap itself around the Axis neck and help
choke the beast to death. (I should add that there are
40,000 additional tank cars " at war " elsewhere in the
country. We couldn't put them all to work in the
East Coast service without dislocating traffic.) Pipe
lines — by far the most efficient method of moving
large volumes of oil overland from the standpoint of
critical materials and power — have at last come into
their own as a means of getting oil to the East Coast

that once depended so exclusively on the tanker. Pipe lines have shortened the distance to the battle fronts and reduced immeasurably the percentage of hazard.

At the outset of the emergency there were, at a rough guess, 126,000 miles of existing pipe lines, which, of course, had not been laid with the possible requirements of a world war in mind. It early became evident that the network had to undergo considerable systematizing in order to meet more nearly military needs. It became the important responsibility of the industry's engineers to rearrange as much of it as was necessary to get the best over-all results. As a result many miles of the pipe-line network east of the Rocky Mountains have been done over to serve the distressed areas. Even before new pipe lines were laid the existing facilities had been relocated and linked together to deliver more than 160,000 barrels toward the East Coast every 24 hours — nearly a 400 per cent increase over the volume carried before the war. This meant diverting the direction of flow in more than 2,000 miles of pipe and the turning about of an additional 800 miles which is now in process. More than 2,000 miles of second-hand pipe have been dug up, salvaged, and relocated. More than 300 miles of natural gas lines have been converted to oil service. To this system has been or is being added 3,400 miles of new lines, all of which will soon be siphoning petroleum products from our oil fields toward the East, and thence to the battle fronts for the duration.

The War Emergency 24-inch Pipe Line — "Big Inch" is the almost affectionate name by which the trade knows it — is the biggest oil line ever built both as to size and capacity. Texas oil is now being run through it to Norris City, Illinois, 531 miles away. Soon it will be dumping oil into 1,000 tank cars daily. This is the equivalent of 20 trainloads of 50 cars each. In addition, the " Big Inch " will feed 50,000 barrels a day into connecting pipe lines. Storage tanks which will hold 1,280,000 barrels are expected to be completed at Norris City by early summer. Tank cars loaded at Norris City today are carrying crude oil, most of which is destined for the New York and Philadelphia harbor districts. Some, however, is going to New England destinations, especially Boston and Providence, although the movement must necessarily be restricted to points at which refineries are located. Later it will carry also " batches " of fuel oil.

The first leg of " Big Inch " was completed in the record-breaking time of less than six months. When extended to New York, and in operation, " Big Inch " will pour 300,000 barrels of oil into the eastern terminals every day of the week, 7 days a week — a grand total of 2,100,000 barrels — nearly 90,000,000 *gallons!* Work on the second leg is well under way. This extension will be 857 miles long and is scheduled for completion sometime in July.

I am too modest to suggest that if " Big Inch " had gone down at the time it was so urgently recommended, we and our allies would be in much better case today with respect to petroleum products. Why? Mainly because the 9,000,000 barrels a month which " Big Inch " could have been delivering over this period would have made it unnecessary for us to draw on our East Coast reserves almost to a vanishing point while readjusting ourselves to the shock of the tanker loss.

Meanwhile, work on another pipe line, to stretch from Houston, Texas, to New York, is under way. This is to be a 20-inch petroleum products line — another vital " blood " stream in our reorganized transportation system to which, as much as to anything else, Herr Hitler may attribute his downfall when it comes.

The expansion of our pipe-line system has meant that thousands of horsepower have been added to the pumping equipment on existing lines in order to boost their " throughput " of oil without other costly time and materials consuming changes.

The shuffling of a pipe-line system in an oil country the size of this one, when geared to the use of oil as this one has been, is truly a colossal undertaking. It commands the attention and the technical knowledge of a hundred of the oil industry's top-flight engineers. Every move, every change, has been made with a view to making the most efficient use of the existing network of the Nation, and with the broad purpose in mind of tying it in with the railroad, barge line, and motor truck facilities. It is in fact an engineering feat as typically American as the Grand Coulee Dam.

When I once reported at a press conference, in response to a question, that a certain pipe line was awaiting the arrival of " a valve," mental visions of a parcel post package may have been conjured up in the minds of some of those present. Not everyone may have been aware that this particular " valve " weighs 7½ tons and stands 12 feet high!

I want it distinctly understood that even with all of the pipe lines working 24 hours a day, 7 days a week, we are not going to be able materially to remove restrictions on our civilian driving. I find a disposition on the part of many people to take it for granted that when the pipe lines are at last delivering up to their capacity, their troubles, so far as gasoline and fuel oil are concerned, will be ended, and the sky will again be the limit.

Let this illusion be dismissed quickly. In the first place, we never would have received approval from WPB for the allocation of steel and critical equipment (nor would we have asked for it) if our purposes were merely to maintain pleasure driving as usual or to eliminate some of the inconveniences that have been visited upon the public.

Of course, no one can look with assurance into the future. We have no way of knowing what the demand from the fighting fronts will be in the distant future, or how soon we will be able to build back our East Coast inventories, badly depleted by heavy winter demands. One of the unforeseeable factors upon which the future of all restrictions hinges is the rate of tanker sinkings in the Atlantic and the volume of tanker capacity that will be available for offshore movement of oil from Atlantic Coast ports direct to the fighting fronts by the shortest route.

The job of supplying our fighters in Europe and

Africa and the Pacific Southwest has just begun and there is little reason to doubt that the demands of the future will far exceed all past and present requirements.

Without our reorganized pipe-line system adjusted to the movements of the railroads and the barges and the motor trucks, and all of them utilized to maximum advantage, we could not hope to move oil in the prodigious volume required.

Inland waterways, too, have played an important part in moving oil since increasingly heavy burdens were placed upon the railroads and coastal shipping was virtually discontinued because of the submarine menace. As a consequence, the rivers and inland waterways have been called upon to transport ever larger volumes of freight. From the start we have recognized the importance of this transportation facility in the movement of oil.

After a thorough survey of the barge and towboat equipment that was available for oil service, steps were taken to put it to work. Operating efficiency was increased through the elimination of delays in transit, a reduction in the time consumed in loading and unloading at terminals, and through the direction of barge movement to dispense with cross hauls so that, with the fewest possible exceptions, barges would move northward and eastward.

The construction of new barges and towboats up to the extent of available steel has gone forward; dry cargo steel barges have been replaced by wooden barges and converted to the service of moving petroleum products; other wooden barges to haul heavy oil have been built; and inland and coastal waterways have been deepened and improved.

Recently considerable agitation has been aroused by proponents of the so-called Trans-Florida Barge Canal. Aside from any geological objections that may have been raised, there are three major considerations involved which are of primary concern to the Petroleum Administration. They are (1) the time which would be required to construct the proposed waterway, (2) the most efficient use which may be made of critical materials and power equipment, and (3) the skilled manpower required.

U. S. Army Engineers have assured me recently that they see no reason to revise their original estimate that such a waterway would require from two to three years to complete. This, in our judgment, would tie up critical materials for an inordinately long time, and might conceivably deprive other more efficient means of transportation, such as pipe lines, of needed critical materials. The steel alone that would be necessary for the canal and the large number of barges, if an appreciable contribution were to be made to the shipment of oil to the East Coast, would be more efficiently used in the construction of pipe lines in the opinion of the Petroleum Administration. Moreover, the obvious need is for improvements that will yield the earliest possible returns. For these main reasons, therefore, I have been opposed to the Florida project.

Petroleum motor transports are responsible for no small part of the increase in the movement of oil to the Atlantic Coast by tank car. Their use has been intensified over the past several months by concentrating their services in the task of releasing tank cars from short-haul distributive activities.

On the average, one motor transport can replace six tank cars in short-haul service. One motor transport unit has been known to take the place of 25 tank cars. Despite the increased cost, oil companies have employed this form of transportation to the full limit of available capacity. Trucks used in place of tank cars have been on a 24-hour schedule, 7 days a week, for the better part of a year. This increased exchange has meant further enlargement of unloading facilities and the complete rearrangement of distribution schedules established over many years of operating experience.

So important are the motor transport units to our activities, that we have encouraged the construction of additional equipment of this type, and are proposing the establishment of a definite production schedule so that replacements for existing units will be on hand.

Although many State regulations controlling the size, weight, and license fees of motor vehicles constitute barriers to the most efficient and fullest use of this means of hauling, it may be that the seriousness of our present transportation bottleneck in petroleum distribution will point the way to at least a temporary abandonment of these impediments.

One Midwest Governor took it upon himself to see that, as one of his State's contributions to the war program, restrictions on oil trucks moving across country through his domain were waived.

It should be recognized that no single one of the transportation units upon which we have had to rely to take the place of the tanker — tank car, tank truck, barge or pipe line — could be operated efficiently except in close relation to the others. Each is playing its big and important part. Taking them all together, and with the fullest cooperation of their personnel, we have been able to develop an intelligent program of coordinated shipping. No small part of the large volume of tank-car movement of oil to the East Coast, for example, has been made possible because the towboats slowly chugging their way up the Mississippi and the Ohio Rivers have brought the oil from the more distant centers of production to tank-car terminals within easier reach of the Atlantic Seaboard.

Streams of oil move underground, silently and invisibly, in ever-increasing daily volume, through the pipe-line network siphoning the midwest and southwest portions of the country, bringing oil all or part of the way to loading terminals where it can be picked up by barge or truck or tank car.

When, therefore, you read about the incredible volume of oil delivered daily to the East Coast by pipe line or railroad tank car, do not forget the part that the barges and the towboats and the motor trucks have played in making it possible.

As I shall have occasion to relate in a subsequent

chapter, one of Hitler's biggest headaches is a transportation system that has not been able to gear itself to meet the emergency.

Heaven be praised! We have thus far been able to accept the challenge!

CHAPTER THREE

Making Ends Meet

In our rush and determination to get enough petroleum to the battle fronts and to the East Coast on time, we had to see to it that adequate supplies were made available for shipment and that there was at the same time a proper balance as between the various products. We had to make ends meet. To have shipped more than the necessary minimum of gasoline to supply requirements would have meant that there might be an insufficiency of fuel oil or not enough crude oil to satisfy the East Coast refineries, many of which are engaged in the manufacture of essential war products. Without supplies to load and a well-balanced apportionment, the ends achieved as the result of our transportation revolution might not have been as good as they were.

We of the Petroleum Administration spent many

sleepless nights over this problem. To do such a job successfully required an intimate knowledge of the availability of petroleum supplies in the Midwest and the Gulf Coast areas, as well as reliable, up-to-the-minute information concerning requirements at every terminal. This knowledge was distilled into information by a Supply Division which was given the responsibility of seeing to it that the essential requirements of each terminal in the eastern region for each petroleum product were met.

Although public recognition has been given to the transportation miracle that has taken place, it is not generally known — except among oil men — that these tremendous readjustments have necessitated equally complex and far-reaching changes in the supply field. To effect these changes, the oil industry was compelled to perform a drastic plastic operation on its normal procedures. It has required a wholesale shift in the supply relationships as between companies, and, had it not been for the most careful planning and the skillful execution of the plans, complete chaos would undoubtedly have resulted. In no other country except America, and, in my opinion, in few other industries could a cooperative undertaking of such gigantic proportions work successfully.

In carrying out this assignment, the Supply Division is assisted by Supply and Distribution Subcommittees in each of the Midwest, East Coast, and Gulf Coast areas. In normal times we have been able to depend upon the automatic operation of competition and the economic relationships of supply and demand to bring about a balanced movement of the right kinds of products to the points where they are needed. But under war conditions the undirected flow of supplies would inevitably fail to achieve first objectives first. For one thing, we are necessarily operating with inventories at minimum levels and with a shortage of transportation capacity. There is, consequently, neither the time nor the means to permit normal corrective processes to accomplish a necessary balance. Moreover, the price structure has been frozen, which has removed another element of flexibility. In the scramble to secure transportation facilities, some companies would have been more successful than others and there would have resulted a serious dislocation of normal business and an unnatural disparity between the various companies as to their ability to transport products in the relative volumes of their customary demand.

With all of these conflicting and complex elements to deal with, it became necessary for the Government, while the war lasted, to take over the intricate job of coordinating the flow of supplies to the East Coast. It has also been necessary to rely upon the knowledge and practical experience of the oil men themselves, and here again there have been very close working relationships. Like a hungry vacuum, the East Coast area has sucked oil, as well as transportation facilities, from the whole region east of the Rocky Mountains, and there is not an oil company operating in that vast area that has not been affected by the operation.

Since the District 1 (East Coast) area is too large to

be treated as a single unit, six supply zones have been established. This enables us to achieve greater efficiency in the scheduling of supplies because it makes it possible for us to give attention to the particular requirements of each zone. Each has a manager and a staff working full time. After a careful survey, terminals were selected so located as to provide an efficient use of transportation facilities and for the equitable redistribution of petroleum products to the companies operating in the area adjacent to the terminals. The industry has appointed representatives for each supply terminal and these representatives work closely with the zone manager and his staff, keeping the latter fully informed as to the disposition of products and the requirements of the terminals.

By means of this petroleum industry network the Petroleum Administration is able to keep itself informed continually of the needs at each key point. This information makes possible the proper routing of supplies so as to keep them balanced throughout the entire district; and when emergency shortages occur, supplies can be quickly rerouted so as to avoid " starvation " for a particular petroleum product in any district. Among the more urgent tasks handled by the Supply and Distribution Subcommittees in the East Coast area is the transfer of stock from one company to another so that scarce products may be evenly distributed within individual zones and even within cities and towns. Let me illustrate:

The U. S. Navy recently informed the Petroleum Administration that it needed a large amount of gasoline at an East Coast port for immediate delivery. The Blank Oil Company which had sufficient gasoline on hand in the vicinity to satisfy the want was asked to make the shipment and did so. This left the Blank Oil Company, however, short of gasoline with which to care for its own customers who were dependent upon it. Arrangements were therefore made with other companies in the region to make available some of their gasoline inventories to it, thereby enabling the Blank Oil Company to make good on its own commitments. The loan was later repaid when some of the other companies ran short on account of unanticipated emergencies. This type of petroleum product "clearing house" makes it possible to minimize the effect of a sudden increase in demand by spreading available inventories. It also makes possible the planning of movements on a regional instead of on a company basis. It has worked out only by the closest cooperation between the companies involved.

Many hours are spent each month by the members of the industry, as well as by the various industry committees and the members of the Petroleum Administration staff, in preparing the numerous schedules required to tie the program together into a well-knit whole. This is one of the principal reasons why it was possible for the petroleum industry to get through the winter of 1942–43 with a minimum of actual suffering by the people of the East Coast. This interrelationship of operations made it possible to reduce inventories to a level which had been considered impossible and which would in fact have been impossible under conditions that had normally prevailed.

Having reduced these inventories generally to their present low levels, we must now undertake the very real task of rebuilding them before the next heating season descends upon us.

In view of the all-time low inventory levels this year, we must realize that we have more storage space to fill than we had a year ago. And more sleepless nights await us before we get it filled.

CHAPTER FOUR

Better to Walk
Than to Freeze

We were beginning to recover from the shock of the tanker loss through the mobilization of other shipping facilities in a drive to get indispensable gasoline and fuel oil into the East Coast area where the first pinch had been felt.

After many headaches, we saw railroad tank cars, barges and motor trucks moving gasoline and fuel oil in ever-increasing volume toward the Atlantic Coast States; we saw a radically reorganized pipe-line network functioning in concert with other transportation facilities and getting bigger on its own account every day.

The herculean job of compensating for the more than a million barrels of petroleum products *a day* that tankers were no longer able to deliver to the East Coast because they had been diverted to war duty or

46

sunk was progressing satisfactorily. The tanker system, that was 30 years in developing, had had to be supplanted quickly by a combination of existing and new carrier facilities. The members of this combination — tank cars, barges, pipe lines, and trucks — are today delivering a volume of petroleum products to and in the general direction of the East Coast that far exceeds the most optimistic forecasts of even a year ago.

Neither the Army nor the Navy has lacked for a gallon of motor fuel, fuel oil, or lubricating oil.

War industries have been supplied and essential civilian requirements have been met.

In other words, we have been able to ship enough essential oil on time despite the almost irreplaceable loss of the services of a tanker fleet that for many years had been bringing in 95 per cent of the East Coast's petroleum.

However, we are still short of the mark. We must bring in still more. We must still replenish our storage stock which, of necessity, we had to draw upon heavily when the tanker life line was cut. But the essential war and civilian needs are being filled.

Because of heavily increased and constantly increasing war requirements, we couldn't, even with all of our shipping replacements, haul enough petroleum into the East Coast to give the people all that they would have used had it been readily available. Even had we been able to offset completely the tanker loss, the volume of petroleum products delivered would not have been enough to fill the potential total demand in the face of the prodigious and growing needs of war industry and of the military forces.

We had, therefore, to eliminate, so far as we could, all unnecessary demands for petroleum products and to restrict unessential consumption. We had to bring demand into balance with the available supply.

The fact that we have been unable to move sufficient oil to fill all needs and at the same time maintain pleasure driving as usual in the Eastern States may obscure from some the full magnitude of our shipping reorganization. This may be because, if we take notice of it at all, we are inclined to take an American success for granted. However, I cannot over-emphasize the fact that had it not been for the exercise of the highest degree of ingenuity, and the most carefully coordinated planning on the part of both the Government and the Petroleum Industry, our predicament today would have been infinitely more serious than it is — and that is too serious for comfort.

I threw out my first warning as far back as June 12, 1941, when in a radio interview I urged the people to drive only when they had to, to drive at a reasonable speed when they did drive, to avoid " jack rabbit starts," and to keep carburetors adjusted so as to get a maximum of efficiency out of them. I urged a voluntary one-third reduction in gasoline consumption. If these things were done, I said, " the pinch won't be so great. There will be a pinch — that is in the cards — but we can ease it considerably by sensible conduct."

Scarcely a day went by for a year after this broadcast that I didn't personally, or through administration channels, plead with the people to use gasoline sparingly and wisely. But most of the time I was as " a voice crying in the wilderness."

Reprinted from the newspaper PM

Giving the Axis a Lift

The driving public, encouraged by newspaper comment to believe that I was talking through my hat, failed to take our recommendations seriously. Instead of buying less gasoline, they hurried out to buy more. So we tried another approach. We ordered filling stations closed between 7 p.m. and 7 a.m. as one possible means of impressing upon the public the seriousness of the problem to be met. And — would you believe it? — the weekly sale of gasoline continued to go up.

We countered by reducing the deliveries of motor fuel to retail outlets. This had the effect of reducing the amount sold by retail outlets to consumers, but, despite some reduction in over-all consumption, too many people were still driving as usual, exceeding speed limits and " jumping the gun " at stop lights.

Here we were watching our tanker supply line from the Texas and Gulf Coast oil fields as it was being cut, and 75 out of 100 motorists were driving hither and yon as if nothing were wrong! Rationing thus became inevitable.

There is little to be gained by reviewing the abuse that was heaped upon my head by newspapers and Congressmen for what they had been misled into believing was the " Ickes bogus oil shortage." A Congressional committee determined well in advance of a complete investigation that there was no shortage either of oil or of transportation, but only a " shortage of surplus." Great sport was had at the expense of the Petroleum Coordinator (later Petroleum Administrator) on the basis of this " verdict." Wisecracks filled the air and the newspapers.

" The Special Committee members," read the preliminary report dated September 11, 1941 (the hearings had only opened August 28 and there had been a 4-day adjournment over Labor Day!) , " like most of the people of the country, were completely satisfied, *from the beginning,* that there was no shortage of petroleum products. . . . The committee furthermore has now concluded that there is no shortage of transportation facilities. . . . The committee members have not attempted to explore *charges of unworthy purposes behind the announced oil 'shortage.'* We have not felt that it was a part of our immediate responsibility to attempt to find out whether or not the ' shortage ' question arose as a result of *a desire to construct a large pipe line, or other pipe lines,* or whether behind the scene there was *some connection with pending anti-trust suits,* or whether the *price of petroleum products was involved.*

" Our conclusions may best be summed up by stating that there is no shortage of petroleum products, nor a shortage, *as of this date,** of transportation facilities, but that the whole frightening picture, from the standpoint of the Coordinator's office, seems to lie in the fact that the shortage, which has excited the activity of the Coordinator, is really a ' shortage ' in a large surplus which is desired. Paradoxical as it sounds, the shortage, as we see it, is a shortage of surplus — and not a shortage of products, or a lack of facilities to transport them." †

That started the jeering all over again, but if you have followed me up to this point, perhaps you have

---

* All italics the author's.

† Recently (February 22, 1943) the Committee published an additional report in which the word *shortage* does not appear in quotes as, at the outset, one member specifically requested be the case whenever he referred to it, presumably as evidence of his low opinion of anyone who said that a shortage existed. The additional report would encourage the belief that the Committee has been on top of the petroleum problem ever since we had one. It also put forward a number of suggestions that had long been in effect.

been able to draw your own conclusions as to the "unworthy purposes" that lurked sinisterly behind our agitation for pipe-line construction and for reasonable driving. It may also have occurred to you that if there was no transportation shortage "as of this date," there was reason to believe that there would be one and that it would have been a smart thing to get ready for it.

To tell you the truth, at the time of the Congressional "investigation" there *was* a shortage of petroleum products because the Atlantic Coast demand was even then on a very rapid rise, and the movement of oil into the area was not in sufficient volume to keep pace with the withdrawals. Tanker shipments were dropping off and we had not yet developed any substantial replacement, with the result that we were falling behind rapidly, and it should have been clear that we couldn't, over an extended period, spend our petroleum products faster than we were replenishing them and expect to stay out of the red. Consumers who had to skimp on their oil last winter were feeling *directly* the effects of that shortage.

There *was* a shortage of transportation as it happened, and as I have attempted to show, because the "20,000" "*idle*" railroad tank cars that were figuratively rattled in front of the Congress and the people of the country did not exist, and *even if they had existed* they couldn't have begun, at least more than temporarily, to take the place of the tankers that were then rapidly dropping out of the East Coast service. In addition to 40,000 tank cars in use in other parts of the country, we now have more than 70,000 cars serving the East Coast which we have drafted, notably from the Middle West, while others have been transferred to oil from other services. The point is, they were *not* idle back in 1941.

And there *was* a shortage of surplus which wasn't half as funny as it may have sounded. As was pointed out to the committee, the so-called shortage was an anticipated deficiency which would not be readily apparent early in the summer when the sun was high in the sky, but would, unless checked, progressively develop into a critical situation as winter approached.

The demand for heating oil is about two and one-half times greater on the East Coast in winter than in summer. It is, therefore, essential that a storage supply be built up during the warm months, when withdrawals are at a minimum, to provide for the winter heating. This has been the normal practice of the industry in the past and it becomes all the more important in the present period when on the one hand transportation capacity is limited, and, on the other, the future outlook is for an increasing war demand.

Which brings me to a point that bears directly on the situation today: Our petroleum stocks on the Atlantic Seaboard are today at an all-time low. Our military future is not adequately protected, and the downward trend of inventory has not yet been halted. The most recent available figures on East Coast oil storage reveal a continued decline of substantial proportions.

In the face of our decidedly unsatisfactory inventory position we cannot conscientiously act to increase the delivery of gasoline for non-essential purposes without a dependable forecast of the supply position over the coming months. This we do not have for the reason that one of the principal factors is the extent of the military demand for offshore shipment. Until we know what is to be required for transshipment to the United Kingdom and North Africa we cannot possibly know what quantities are to be available for home consumption. We expect soon to have figures as to the future military requirement, but in the absence of such information we can form no reliable judgment as to what lies ahead. And, in any event, we must be prepared — with storage tanks full — for whatever emergency demands the military forces may make upon us. We can afford to take no chances.

Aside from the military requirement, which is the principal unknown factor, and one that in the nature of things cannot be predicted with too great certainty, there are other factors to be considered as well. What tank car performance can be looked for in the fair weather period is a matter of estimate and is bound up with complex questions as to the availability of supplies at the different possible sources.

Taking all of these factors into account, we have to determine whether the people want to do more " driving as usual " this summer or to do more " freezing than usual " next winter. We have decided — and, I think, wisely — against the " driving as usual."

The job of the Petroleum Administration is to make available the greatest possible volume of petroleum products for any given period. It is then up to others to say how it is to be apportioned. I still think that, if required to make a choice, the average person would choose heating oil over gasoline. A man can walk or ride a bus, but he can't be even reasonably comfortable in an unheated house, and how many men are there who are willing to go to work and leave their families home to shiver?

We have the same problem that we had last summer of replenishing our East Coast stocks, both of fuel oil and of gasoline. Both are well below the level of what the oil industry considers the danger line. We have to bring in much more fuel oil this summer than we were required to bring in last summer if only to get our stocks back to the level that they were when we went into the heating season last fall and which, incidentally, was too low. I cannot believe that people in New England, for instance, want to go through another winter with less fuel than they had last winter. That they would like at least as much I am sure.

I wish sincerely that we could furnish enough petroleum for everybody, both for driving and living comfort, while at the same time maintaining a steady flow of it to the battle fronts and to our war industries. But since that is an impossibility under present conditions, it becomes somebody's job to say what takes precedence over what. Few of us will disagree that unessential driving is at the end of the list. It would therefore seem wise to take the position that we will have no gasoline for unnecessary purposes. How unessential driving may be eliminated — whether by so-called " bans " or by reductions in the value of coupons — is a matter that is not within the jurisdiction of the Petroleum Administration.

The question of gasoline rationing has been further complicated and confused in the public mind because gasoline today is rationed in different parts of the United States for two separate and quite unrelated reasons. On the one hand, in areas where there is a physical shortage of gasoline or of transportation to provide it, rationing has been instituted for the purpose of conserving the available supply and of assuring an equitable distribution to consumers. Thus far, this kind of gasoline rationing exists only in 17 States on the Atlantic Seaboard and in the District of Columbia. The degree of rationing there is greater than elsewhere in the country. Throughout the remainder of the United States the so-called "nation-wide gasoline rationing" is in effect for the purpose of conserving rubber. Instead of rationing transportation directly, it was decided to restrict the motor fuel without which, of course, motor vehicles cannot operate. In certain areas there were times when there was such an abundance of gasoline that its storage became a critical problem. People in such areas found it difficult to understand why, with tanks virtually running over, the supplies of gasoline available to them were restricted.

The Pacific Northwest area presents its own distinctive problem. There it is necessary to rely principally on tankers to bring oil from California. Overland transportation facilities are not good and there are no pipe lines and no barges, although limited supplies do come in by rail from Montana and Wyoming.

Tank cars have been used to some extent for emergency deliveries, but most of the railroad lines between the oil fields and the Pacific Northwest are a single track heavily loaded with war freight, and the volume of oil that can be moved in this way is therefore limited. In order to release as many tankers as possible for war duty, it was necessary to impose fuel oil restrictions on space and central heating and hot water supply as in the East Coast and the Middle West. Gasoline rationing, too, was put into effect in March 1942 by limiting deliveries to suppliers. This restriction was lifted in December 1942 when the so-called nation-wide consumer-gasoline rationing became effective.

But it is the fuel oil situation that hits us harder generally than even the gasoline problem. Not only is fuel oil vitally necessary to keep the wheels of war industry turning, and to bunker the many ships of the Navy and those that carry war goods to the fighting fronts, but fuel for heating homes, offices and factories touches closely the welfare and well-being of so many civilians, especially children, invalids, and the infirm who must remain indoors. Moreover, it is important that essential war workers be not subjected to unusual exposure at a time when good health is such a factor.

In normal times the Atlantic Coast area depended upon foreign importations of fuel oil from Caribbean sources. Something like 40,000,000 barrels of fuel oil a year were normally imported, together with substantial quantities of crude oil of heavier grades. To illustrate how important this additional fuel supply was to the East Coast, I might point out that in 1941 importations accounted for approximately 23 per cent of the total East Coast supply. During the winter months of heavy fuel demand, importations increased to as much as one-third of the total. We had come to rely upon this fuel from the Caribbean area to round out our domestic supplies. Because of the diversion of tankers to the military service, this source of fuel oil has been to a great extent cut off. The result has been to place a heavy additional burden upon our domestic refiners.

In addition to reorganizing the transportation system and the imposing of restrictions upon space and central heating and hot water supply as a means of making available more fuel oil products for shipment east, we attacked the problem in another way, i.e., by directing the refiners in the Midwest, East Coast, and Gulf Coast areas to alter their refinery operations so as to produce more of the vitally needed fuel and heating oils and proportionately less gasoline of which, as I have said, there is a sufficient supply. It should be borne in mind that there is considerable flexibility in the refining operation and this makes it possible to shift yields as between the various products that are refined. The whole question of refinery yields is highly complex and technical, and I mention it here only by way of illustrating the fact that we have explored all of the possibilities — on the one hand, reducing consumption to equalize the shortage burden, and on the

other, altering refinery operations to increase the supply of the particular products that are in greatest
demand.

At the same time, the clamor for fuel oil, especially
on the Atlantic Coast, has increased substantially. Our
war plants are making more and more heavy inroads
upon the available supply, and large volumes of fuel
are required for bunkering ships along the Atlantic
Seaboard. In addition, we have been called upon to
supply ever-increasing amounts of fuel oil for offshore
shipment.

A combination of these factors has given rise to an
acute shortage of fuel oil supplies, particularly in the
heavier grades. We are confronted here with a shortage
of supplies themselves, and not with just a shortage of
transportation facilities.

In our transportation revolution we find the source
of many confusing issues, among them the bewilder-
ment of some Midwesterners when it became necessary to introduce fuel oil rationing in that area. It is
axiomatically American that when the people understand why certain things are done they grin and bear
them without further complaint. Therefore, I want to
devote some space to the Midwest fuel oil rationing
problem.

As the 70,000 railroad tank cars have been pressed
into East Coast service, it has become essential that
the most efficient use be made of them. They have had
to be run in trainload lots, schedules have had to be
speeded up, quick turns-around have had to be ar-

ranged, and, as important as anything else, the cars have had to be routed and operated over the shortest distances.

From the Midwest to New York, it is, roughly, 1,000 miles; from the Gulf Coast, it is, also roughly, 2,000 miles. It is estimated that two cars delivering to the Atlantic Coast from Midwest points can haul as much as three tank cars traveling between the Gulf Coast and the East. This made obvious the fact that the efficient thing to do was to haul from the Midwest as much oil as could be made available.

To give you an idea of the effect of the shorter hauls on the Midwest situation, I need only point out that as compared with the month of September 1941, when 12,000 barrels of residual fuel oil and 37,000 barrels of distillate oil were shipped eastward from the Midwest, the deliveries from the Midwest in September of 1942 increased to 2,370,000 barrels of residual fuel and to 1,538,000 barrels of distillate oil.

As we began to run more and more tank cars over shorter routes, a shortage of available supply developed in the Midwest area. There wasn't enough oil there to take care of the local markets and at the same time to fill all of the tank cars that had been made available for service to the East Coast.

Now the major part of the Nation's productive and refining capacity is in the more remote Gulf area, and from that point there were not enough pipe lines, barges or other carrier facilities to move crude or fuel oil to the Midwest in the volume required. Consequently, restrictions upon space and central heating and hot water supply in the Middle West became necessary in order to spread the burden more equitably over the East Coast and Middle West areas. Certainly it would not have been fair to permit citizens of the East Coast to suffer an even more serious shortage in order that people living in the Midwest might continue to have oil to meet all peacetime requirements. Consumption in the Midwest was not restricted on the theory that " misery loves company " or because we hoped that those living on the East Coast would like us better if we imposed equalizing inconveniences on some of the other sections of the country. It was the only way to move the maximum volume of critically needed supplies to the Eastern Seaboard over the shortest and most efficient routes. It was also the only possible way of preventing extreme suffering in the East.

Almost two years ago I announced that to help ease the East Coast situation it would be necessary to use transportation facilities from other areas and that, as a consequence, the effect upon the Midwest would be serious.

It was in the fall of 1941 that this office forecast a shortage of residual fuel oil in the Eastern States, in which territory the projected normal consumption was approximately 150,000,000 barrels per annum.

At that time we asked all residual fuel oil suppliers in that area to send us a list of their consumers whose annual volume was in excess of 25,000 barrels. We also asked for a statement as to the conversion possibilities of each of these consumers from fuel oil to coal or other fuel.

With lists totaling approximately 20,000 industrial and commercial consumers, we began a direct mail campaign in the Atlantic Coast area for the conversion of heating plants from fuel oil to coal or other available substitute fuel. This campaign required the writing of some 3,000 letters a week for approximately five months. It necessitated our having at our disposal trained engineers and petroleum analysts who were thoroughly familiar with the problem before us. These men were all recruited from the petroleum industry.

Our conversion program was supplemented by semi-monthly press releases, radio broadcasts, promotional commercial announcements that were made through the medium of petroleum industry programs, as well as by group meetings and personal discussions, all of them being directed to the necessity of conversion to coal and the conservation of fuel oils.

As the situation in the East became more critical, it became necessary to extend the conversion campaign to the Midwestern States. In a public statement at that time, we declared that it was important that all fuel oil consumers in the Midwest realize that the situation was so uncertain that we could give them no assurance that their full requirements of fuel oil could be supplied. The appeal was directed particularly to users of industrial fuel oils since it had been estimated that at least 20,000,000 barrels of industrial fuel oil could be saved annually by conversions in the Mid-western States.

For almost two years we have been endeavoring by every possible means to convince the public that it would become impossible to meet all demands for residual and distillate fuel oils. We have continually urged all consumers — both householders and users of the heavier grades of oil who could do so — to convert to coal or to other available fuels.

Although conversions have not proceeded at as rapid a pace as had been hoped for, nevertheless, a large share of the credit for meeting last winter's fuel oil supply, rationed though it was, must be given to those foresighted home and plant owners — Eastern-ers and Midwesterners — who did convert from fuel oil to other fuels. The savings thus effected made it possible to avoid what otherwise would have been a disastrous situation.

The latest figures on the normal fuel oil consump-tion and conversion results in the East (District 1) and the Midwest (District 2) are enlightening. They show that in District 1 where the total estimated pos-sible industrial conversions were 66 per cent of the total normal consumption, 27 per cent of that total have been converted to the use of coal or other fuels.

In District 2 the results have not been quite so re-sponsive but they are still not bad. Out of a total pos-sible conversion estimated at 27 per cent of the total normal consumption, 14 per cent have converted to coal or other fuel.

In the Middle West 986 industrial consumers had converted up to the time that this was written, with the resultant saving of approximately 7,250,000 barrels of fuel oil annually. Conversions that are now under way will result in the saving of 3,000,000 more barrels.

During the past 12 months, 6,000 industrial consumers on the Eastern Seaboard have converted, resulting in an annual saving of 40,500,000 barrels of residual fuel oil, and additional conversions are now under way which will save an additional 2,500,000 barrels annually.

Our ultimate goal is to increase the existing industrial oil savings of 40,500,000 barrels in the East and 7,250,000 barrels in the Midwest to 65,000,000 and 16,000,000, respectively.

To date more than 120,000 homeowners in the East have converted their oil fired heating plants at a total yearly saving of at least 6,000,000 barrels. The number of homeowners in the Middle West who have changed has been relatively small. However, with industrial conversions of 47,750,000 barrels, plus the domestic conversions of more than 6,000,000 barrels, the total switch from fuel oil to other fuels in the two areas represent a saving of more than 53,000,-000 barrels per year. This is approximately 19 per cent of the total fuel oil consumed in the two districts.

It is believed that the hardships that have been undergone by domestic consumers of oil by reason of rationing will convince many more that they should change their facilities during the summer months. We are making arrangements accordingly through the

WPB to see that sufficient equipment will be made available. It is my opinion that a heating program should be predicated upon the probability that the war will drag into the years of 1944 and 1945.

When a householder or a factory head has decided to change to coal, he has taken only the first important step. Almost as important as the decision itself is his early ordering of coal.

The mines of the country operate without storage facilities, so that the coal produced in any given day must be shipped *on order* to a destination where it can be consumed or stored. Unless the mine has the orders on hand for each day's supply as it is produced, it slowly closes down because the only place to store unsold coal is in railroad cars which, in no circumstances, should be used for such purposes.

The 13,000 soft coal mines of the country are expected to produce for consumption and export the estimated requirement of 600 million tons for 1943. The 250 hard coal mines of Pennsylvania are expected to meet the need for 63 million tons of anthracite.

All of this must be moved when and as it is brought up out of the ground, and it is up to the consumers to provide the storage space for it. Otherwise the consumer who has converted his heating plant may not be able to get the coal when he wants it for the burner that is no longer adapted to the consumption of oil. Not a pleasant thought, but necessary to consider.

For industrial plants equipped with steam atomizing burners and with some models of the automatic rotary type burner, a substitute fuel for residual fuel oil where conversion cannot be made will be available within a few months. This substitute fuel is a mixture of 60 per cent fuel oil and 40 per cent coal which is ground up in particles to a size not exceeding 30 microns, which is about twice as fine as flour.

Although this colloidal fuel is not adaptable for household heating systems, it is believed that, with the completion of the proposed colloidal plants in October, a saving at the rate of 15,000,000 barrels per year of residual fuel oil can be accomplished by industries in Districts 1 and 2.

The principal advantage of colloidal fuel is that there is an increase in the heat value of approximately 3 per cent, plus a saving in fuel oil of 40 per cent. Colloidal fuel is sufficiently fluid to be placed in storage tanks at the point of production, pumped to loading racks into trucks, barges or tank cars, then into storage tanks. It is so fluid, also, that the coal remains in suspension and does not settle. It may be pumped through piping to the burner in the same manner as residual fuel oil is now handled. The use of colloidal fuel would be a contribution to safety because of the fact that it is heavier in specific gravity than water and, in the event of a ruptured tank, the spreading of fire would be controlled by the application of water alone. In addition, were it used for fuel in marine work and for any reason the bunkers were ruptured, the fuel would not spread fire on the surface of the water because it would immediately sink below the level of the sea.

I think that it is a good thing for us as individuals to remember, when we are inclined to kick about rationing, that it is actually our best protection against discrimination. Without such restrictions and regulations, we might easily fail to get our fair share in the distribution of a commodity for which there is such a clamorous demand as there is for gasoline and fuel oil.

The individual citizen does not, I know, begrudge a drop of the petroleum that goes to war, and if his Government didn't put all of it that is necessary into the fight, he would be the first to yell " murder." And with good reason. What remains after that for civilian consumption can only be fairly distributed on a basis which takes into account relative degrees of essentiality.

Gradually, we are becoming convinced that the cumulative effect of a great many small savings — of a conversion to a substitute fuel, of a room shut off, of a car driven only when necessary — represents a substantial contribution to victory. It is here behind the lines that the questions are asked; on the fighting front it is " but to do or die."

If those of us at home would but try to understand the many ramifications of the problem of producing and shipping and equalizing the consumption of essential petroleum products, criticism of the administration of it would not be a matter of politics; nor would it be based upon individual inequities that are bound to occur in the most favorable circumstances. Moreover, there would be an increasing appreciation of the fact that the Government and the oil industry are pulling together in a mighty and all-engrossing effort to " keep 'em flying " over there and to " keep the home fires burning " over here.

CHAPTER FIVE

Partners

in Oil

If I were asked to name the most important *intangible* contribution to the success of our wartime petroleum problem, I would unhesitatingly point to the cooperation that has existed between the Government and the Oil Industry from the outset.

It was by a strange coincidence that the first meeting of the Petroleum Industry War Council, a meeting which we had called ten days before, happened to convene a few hours after the Japanese attack on Pearl Harbor.

I have looked into some pretty grim visages in my day — bankers who have been asked for a loan, U. S. Senators frying the fat out of a witness — but if Hideki Tojo could have sat where I did on that certain bleak December morning and peered into the faces that were all about me, he might have wished that he had slept another night or two on the proposal to bomb Hawaii. And had someone asked me, " what's cooking? " I could have answered truthfully — " the Japanazi goose, of course." For it certainly was.

The relationship now existing between the Government and the Petroleum Industry demonstrates, beyond dispute, that Government and Industry can work together, although it has taken a war to prove it. In terms of human affairs the machinery that I am about to describe is unique. Nothing like it, I believe, has ever been attempted, much less achieved.

We have issued no fiat or ukase. No dictatorship exists or impends. We — the Government and the Petroleum Industry — had been working in close harmony for many months, but on that memorable morning of December 8, 1941, we really became full-fledged partners in a total war on a common enemy, and the partnership will not be dissolved until the war is won. After Pearl Harbor we really took off our gloves, rolled up our sleeves, and started " swinging from the cellar."

Early in the summer of 1941, following my appointment as Petroleum Coordinator for National Defense (later changed to Petroleum Administrator for War) , I had issued an open invitation to oil men from all parts of the country — representatives of small and large companies, as well as individual operators — to meet with me in Washington and discuss the coordination of their industry. It seemed to me that my first step was to talk things over with the men with whom I would inevitably be in contact and upon whom I would have to rely if I were physically to get my new job done.

You may or may not recall that I.had had some differences of opinion with the industry a few years back on the subject of conservation. The well-known *entente cordiale* had been seriously strained. The atmosphere that prevailed as we foregathered on that summer day back in '41 was pretty much the same that one might find just before a mutineer was to be strung up to the mizzenmast. I was held to be a very bad character, indeed; an unhealthy influence on our national life; one who went about looking for industries that he could clamp chains on.

It may have been my imagination, but I thought, as I entered the room, that someone quickly but deftly frisked me for concealed weapons. I thought that I saw one of the oil men looking out of the window to determine, I suspected, his chances for making a quick get-away. It was a pretty tense moment.

After all it was not to be wondered at that the oil men had their fingers crossed when our meeting was called to order. Wasn't I one of the more toxic of the New Dealers? Didn't I look with suspicion on anyone who made a profit? Didn't I believe that Government should rule business with a blacksnake? Wasn't I the " so-and-so " who had tried to take over the oil industry back in 1934? And, finally, hadn't I aspired to be an Oil Czar?

To move a little ahead of my story, I can best describe what our relations were and what they developed into by quoting William R. Boyd, Jr., President of the American Petroleum Institute and Chairman of the Petroleum Industry War Council, who said to a Congressional committee about a year ago:

" I would not be frank with you," Mr. Boyd testified, " if I did not say that the appointment of Secretary Ickes as Petroleum Coordinator, at that time, was viewed throughout the producing branch of the industry in particular with considerable alarm. You . . . know of the historical scraps between the industry and the Secretary of the Interior over legislative proposals which he sponsored or recommended. He called these proposals conservation measures; we in the industry called them regimentation and Federal control. . . . We told you with all the vigor we could command that he was a would-be Oil Czar."

In the course of the same testimony, Mr. Boyd told of some of the experiences which my Office and the industry had been through between the time of our initial meeting and the date of his testimony — February 17, 1942. He concluded:

" It gives me great pleasure to testify here in commendation of the fine, patriotic, intelligent, effective work being done by the Office of Petroleum Coordinator, and those directing and associated with it.. The rather rare thing of staffing a government agency with men who are actually engaged in the business with which such government agency deals is novel but effective."

And while I am pinning on myself medals coined by another, I may as well mention that, unaccustomed as I am to getting compliments, the one that I prize most was voiced by a representative of the industry who avowed that " Ickes would himself have made a great oil man."

But to get back to the first meeting — after some preliminary discussion, we gradually got our feet under the same table without anyone breaking a leg. We agreed, at the beginning at least, to go through the motions of cooperating. From that modest start came the appointment, by me, of a series of district committees to consult with and advise the Office on any and all problems having to do with oil in the war. I was careful to establish a fair balance as between small and large companies, and in all cases to choose men who had the confidence and respect of their fellow oil men.

Later, using the chairmen of the district committees as the nucleus, we organized the Petroleum Industry Council for National Defense, a name officially changed later to Petroleum Industry War Council. This was the Council which, by historic coincidence, held its first meeting in Washington on the day after Pearl Harbor. It was thus our good fortune to be organized for war on the very day that war came to us.

In the meantime I had prevailed upon Ralph K. Davies of San Francisco, ranking Vice President of the Standard Oil Company of California, to come to Washington for the duration as a full-time Government employee. He became the Deputy Coordinator, later Deputy Administrator. I told Mr. Davies that I wanted him to employ the best men that he could find

— to get men from the industry — men who *knew oil*.

So successfully has Mr. Davies carried out the responsibility that I put upon his shoulders that there is
not today any oil company in the world with a better
technical staff than the one that is now working with
the Government to win the Battle of Oil. I will have
more to say of this a little later on in this chapter.

At this point I wish to go on record with the asser-
tion that in all of my years of contact with business
leaders — including my days as Public Works Administrator when I was responsible for the expenditure of
more than 6 billion dollars — I have never encountered greater loyalty or more unselfish devotion to a
job, or more intelligent cooperation, than I have found
in this same Ralph K. Davies. The country owes much
to him for his contribution to the development and
the operation of the petroleum program.

I had said to the oil men: " Let us get one thing
straight, right now. I don't want to run your industry.
If we can't work this out cooperatively, there is something wrong with us. In this effort, the oil industry
needs the aid of the Government, and the Government needs the aid of the oil industry. It is a joint task.
There are no ' Hitlers over here.' Let's go."

We divided the country into five regions — East
Coast, Middle West, Gulf Coast-Southwest, Rocky
Mountain, and Pacific Coast. In each region we proceeded to set up industry committees to consult with
and to advise with us as to the principal oil operations
— production, natural gas and natural gasoline, refining, transportation, and marketing. The chairmen

of these committees, together with a general chairman, were constituted a general committee for each district, to work upon problems which involved more than one of the enumerated functions, and to coordinate industry activities within the district.

We wanted to be as certain as possible that these committees would be truly representative of the industry as a whole. So we called for nominations from the entire industry, and upon these nominations, the committees were based. With a dozen men on each committee, we thus have sixty representative oil leaders in each district — 300 for the Nation as a whole — working with us continually on the multifold and worrisome task of making oil do its indispensable job in the war. In addition to the members of these committees, hundreds of other men have been appointed to membership on subcommittees that have been established to make studies and recommendations on specific problems, or to carry into effect the programs that have been officially approved by the Government.

It was inevitable, I suppose, that in asking the oil companies to plan jointly to meet the wartime emergencies most efficiently, and possibly even to pool their facilities and products, we might be inviting them to take steps that would raise questions under the antitrust laws. A similar problem had already arisen with respect to industry group action under the aegis of the Office of Production Management and a procedure had been evolved betwen that Office and the Department of Justice whereby general programs involving concerted industry functions were submitted to the Attorney General and cleared by the Justice Department before being carried into effect. We early reached an agreement with the Attorney General for an extension of this treatment to industry programs carried out under the direction and supervision of the Petroleum Administration.

I want to make one thing emphatically clear. These are *not* rubber stamp committees. Anyone who knows oil men will understand that " yes-ing " is contrary to their nature. And anyone who knows me is aware that yes-men are among my heartiest aversions. Let us be frank. Our early meetings with these committees were not love feasts. There was, as I have acknowledged freely, an atmosphere of suspicion. The oil men were not quite sure what I was up to. They suspected that it was something of which they wouldn't approve. They were not quite certain that there wasn't an entrapment somewhere. They were more than a little skeptical as to the workability of the committee plan. The sum total of these factors was an undercurrent of resistance. It distinctly was not a case of love at first sight. Nor at second sight, either. So, during the " honeymoon," there was a good deal of sparring — and some slugging. And then, gradually, there began to dawn the realization that this wasn't purely another marriage of convenience. Maybe this fellow, Ickes, wasn't dealing from a cold deck after all. And maybe these oil magnates knew how to work in harness. There was a general awakening.

The cooperative idea took hold. It worked. It worked so well that, during the fall, we decided to carry it further. The district committees had functioned adequately on regional matters, but an increasing number of our problems had national ramifications that called for a grouping which could operate on a national scale. Therefore, I appointed 72 leaders of the industry as the Petroleum Industry Council for National Defense, later rechristened the Petroleum Industry War Council. Like the industry committees, it represents both large and small interests. In addition, it has representatives of oil associations and co-operatives.

This Council was appointed November 28, 1941, and the first meeting was held ten days later. Thus I was responsible for what a member of the Council termed " one of the great coincidences of history." The first meeting, as I have said, was held the day after Pearl Harbor.

It was one of the most dramatic occasions that I ever expect to experience. As we assembled expectantly, a shocked Nation was tensely trying to get its bearings. The President had not yet gone before the Congress to ask for the formal declaration of a state of war. Two hours later we adjourned to a radio room to hear the President's epochal speech in which he asked Congress to declare a state of war with Japan. Every man present felt that the oil industry was already mobilized for a war in which the future of America itself was at stake. As I looked about the room, I had two dominant impressions — a solemn realization of the enormity of the task ahead, and an almost exhilarating *sureness* that those men around the conference table would see to it that their country had every barrel of oil that it needed for victory. I sensed then — and subsequent events have fully borne me out — that, however bitterly they may have fought each other, or me, in peacetime, they were at last united for as long as it would take to give the Axis a first-class licking.

Around the table were the big names of the industry, heads of the powerful integrated companies whose brands are still familiar to every motorist. Yes, and also around the table were the leading independents, and, with them, men whose names the average citizen would not recognize if he heard them — names that meant, however, that the " little fellow " had just as much voice on this Council as the so-called majors — *and as many votes.*

The Council has the same freedom of action as the district committees. It can discuss any subject that it chooses and make any recommendation that it desires. Moreover, we have an understanding that our Office will take no major action until we first submit the matter to the Council for its criticism and suggestions. We find that we avoid a lot of trouble by availing ourselves of the judgment of these practical men of the industry. As a matter of fact, on all major problems, we call in the industry and say: " Here is the knot — tell us how to untie it."

The full Council meets once a month, usually for two days, and sometimes for longer, and always without compensation. The committees and subcommittees are working virtually every day. They have done their job so patriotically, so effectively, that the oil industry has already assured itself of a chapter of honor in the history of this war.

Of similar effectiveness is the Foreign Operations Committee which meets every two weeks, with sub-committees meeting at more frequent intervals, to handle foreign problems in much the same way that the War Council handles domestic problems. Concerning this group, I will have more to say in another chapter.

I wish to pay tribute here to William Boyd, Jr., Chairman of the Council, whose effective work has contributed substantially to the success of the Government-Industry partnership.

While the oil men of the country were organizing themselves for the biggest job that they had ever been called upon to undertake, we were getting ourselves organized within. As I have said, Mr. Davies had taken leave of private life, temporarily severed his connections with the Standard Oil Company of California, and moved in with me. Naturally he began recruiting his staff largely from the petroleum industry because, generally speaking, he knew that he would have to obtain from that quarter alone the men who possessed the necessary technical background and practical experience with oil operations. These men were drawn from the ranks of the small companies as well as from the large, and from all parts of the country. Mr. Davies and I both felt that the best way to handle the oil problem was to surround ourselves with men who understood it backwards as well as forwards.

The oil industry today is a highly technical, complex, and delicately adjusted affair. There was a time when it involved only a simple drilling operation to get the crudes, and relatively simple distillation to get the products. Now we require geologists, geophysicists, and paleontologists in the field; chemists, physicists, and engineers in the refinery; traffic experts, economists, analysts, and highly trained organizers and executives in transportation and distribution. Outside of the personnel of the industry itself there is but little understanding of the finely balanced and intricately interrelated mechanisms of the production, refining, transportation, and marketing of petroleum.

As we proceeded with the task of coordinating oil operations for the war, we ourselves had ample reason to become more and more conscious of these complexities and intricacies as they applied to the full range of the petroleum industry. In our job of bringing the half million units of the industry fully into the war program, we had to be mindful constantly of this sensitivity to dislocations which, to the layman, seem inconsequential. For each of the approximately 400,-000 oil wells, there is, by coincidence, a retail outlet, or 400,000 of them, and between the wells and the outlets is a network of transportation shuttling between the oil fields, refineries, and the market. We had to act with full awareness that changes in production conditions in one field might — and often did — affect other fields; that shifts in refinery operations, if not properly made, could unbalance other operations, back to the fields of production or forward to the division of distribution.

We knew that this work of adjustment as applied to petroleum and particularly to petroleum at war was no work for the inexperienced and the uninitiated. It was a job for experts. The adjustments had to be accomplished with the fine instruments and the skill required to perform a delicate operation. Only so could a truly successful result be achieved. There was a greater need for the forceps and scalpel and the skilled surgeon than for the meat ax and the hack saw and the clumsy butcher.

It was in recognition of these facts that I acted to make full use of the talent of the industry itself. The vast industrial organization associated with the Petroleum Administration was put together with this in mind and the staffs of the Washington and the 5 district offices were selected on the same basis.

We are now engaged in decentralizing the activities of the Petroleum Administration to the greatest practical extent, giving to our district offices increased authority to deal with oil problems locally. Within a general framework of established policy this will make it possible for the oil industry to have its problems handled directly and quickly.

The Petroleum Administration exists for the primary purpose of furnishing simple direction to the oil industry during the war period. It is now clear, I believe, to everyone that without such a central agency of Government, guiding and coordinating the efforts of the oil industry, the great task which will continue to face us in oil could not possibly be performed. The requirements of the Nation must be ascertained by this central governmental organization; they must be interpreted to the various units of the industry; the necessary allocation of materials must be arranged in proper relation to other competing demands; and plans must be furnished and executed to attain the equivalent of the consolidated operation of the many units of the industry which, in normal times, work best in independent competition, but in time of war must be banded together to meet the immediate necessities of the period.

The work of adjusting the economy of oil to the requirements of the Nation at war can only succeed in the fullest sense when the industry gives its complete cooperation. The Government could not hope to put together any organization which could supplant that built by the industry over the past 75 years. This I have recognized from the outset and our work has been undertaken, therefore, in the spirit of a wartime partnership between Industry and Government — brought together to make oil do its full part in winning the war. I am happy to attest to the fact that the cooperation of the partnership has left nothing to be desired. Today it exists as a going concern successfully carrying on one of the Nation's great war assignments.

Because it was organized and ready for business early, the Petroleum War Council was able to undertake, at the specific request of the President, the direction of the scrap rubber drive last summer. Only recently the last of the 454,155 tons collected at that time was shipped to the purchasers designated by the Rubber Reserve Corporation.

In that campaign, where speedy mobilization was an essential factor, the oil companies enlisted approximately 1,000,000 of their men and women employees to do the work. They turned their 400,000 filling stations into collection depots; they used their trucks to haul the scrap; they conducted an extensive advertising and publicity campaign out of their own funds; and only recently divided $2,500,000 equally between the United Service Organizations, the Army Relief, the Navy Relief, and the Red Cross, the proceeds of their sale to the Rubber Reserve purchasing agents.

My original appointment by the President as Petroleum Coordinator gave me the right only to *try to persuade* individuals and Government agencies to let us do what we thought ought to be done. No one was required to listen to me — more often than not people took full advantage of the option — and I had no authority that permitted me to exercise my always restless initiative. Of course, I never have performed at my best " under wraps," so I began snitching a little liberty here and a little there until results justified more and more liberal interpretations of the President's wishes. The first thing that anyone knew I was making myself disagreeable enough to be actually getting things done. Then came the President's Executive Order designating me as the Petroleum Administrator which, while it does not give me all of the authority with respect to petroleum, has permitted me to come out from behind my disguise and pound the table with more certainty that I would have an attentive audience.

It may be true, as some Congressmen have contended, that the Petroleum Administrator is still lacking all of the authority that he needs, but I have no hesitancy in saying that this is an issue that will in no case alter the relationship between the Petroleum Administration, representing the Government, and the petroleum industry. When the emergency ends, the authority that I possess as Petroleum Administrator will be promptly shed.

While on this subject, I am constrained to say that the relationship between official Washington and the petroleum industry, working together in a national emergency, may well serve as the post-war pattern for a more understanding relationship between the Government and all business. I do not mean to say that we have had no differences — that after the first few embarrassing moments we have been holding hands and looking at each other in unaffected admiration. We disagree on many subjects. Occasionally we have found ourselves bumping into each other. The oil men take issue with the Government and with each other, but what could be healthier?

The petroleum industry is a highly competitive one. Apropos of this is the story of a submarine that suddenly appeared in a convoy of tankers creating, as you may guess, quite a disturbance. The tankers started going in every direction. In the confusion a tanker of one company rammed amidship a tanker of a rival, causing quite a bit of damage. When informed of it, Deputy Administrator Davies remarked dryly: " They should forget their rivalry in these trying times! "

We have demonstrated in the treatment of the petroleum problem during wartime that Government and business, both large and small, can work together on a common ground of mutual trust and understanding, without fear, on the one hand, that confiscation impends, and without suspicion, on the other, that all of the cards are not on the table, face up.

CHAPTER SIX

Doing More with Less

I would call attention to the fact that with the biggest job in its history to do — with the outcome of a world war depending largely on its products — the oil industry, in common with others, has been operating under the double handicap of material and manpower shortages.

In the case of petroleum, this imposes an unusually severe strain. To maintain production levels the industry must engage in extensive drilling of discovery wells and in developing existing fields; it must increase the production of vital war products such as 100-octane gasoline, toluene for explosives, and butadiene for synthetic rubber; it must assure the continued flow of gasoline and fuel oil in ever-increasing volume; and it must make certain of adequate transportation and distribution facilities for the delivery of petroleum products to areas where and when they are required.

These things call for critical materials at a time when critical materials are very difficult to obtain.

The individual who is rationed learns to adjust himself. If it relates to gasoline, he drives less. If food is involved, he eats less, or changes his diet. If it is a matter of materials, he delays the execution of his plans until a better day.

Industry, however, is totally dependent upon the free flow of materials. Although it can and does develop many substitutes, it simply must have huge quantities of steel and similar critical materials in order to do its job. If it is denied materials beyond essential requirements, it suffers more than mere inconvenience. It is unable to perform its vital functions in the war program.

At the outbreak of the war, there were literally thousands of planes, tanks, motor vehicles, and ships that had to have gasoline and lubricating oil, *or else*. It fell to the lot of the petroleum industry to deliver —also, *or else*. As time went on the problem became immeasurably greater and more complicated, and the materials with which to overcome it became less.

I do not doubt that other industries have had comparable trials, but the troubles of the oil industry are the ones that I happen to be most familiar with. That may be why I seem to give out the impression — if I do — that the oil industry is having the hardest struggle of all.

During 1942 the petroleum industry received,

roughly speaking, less than half of the tonnage of steel and fabricated goods that it was able to obtain the year before. Even granted that the industry made abnormally large purchases in 1941, it is still true that it is now required to operate under war conditions with from one-half to one-third less materials than in normal times.

To meet the greatly expanded requirements for petroleum products with such a drastic reduction in materials has been a problem of the first magnitude. But by careful management, plus a high degree of resourcefulness and ingenuity — by doing more with less, in other words — the petroleum industry has been able to perform its functions in the war program in the face of unusual difficulties.

Under the Controlled Materials Plan, the Petroleum Administration has been established as a Claimant Agency. This means that we have been made responsible for presenting the requirements of the petroleum industry for materials and for effecting the proper distribution of such materials as may be allotted by the War Production Board for the industry's use.

One of the most important links in this chain of activity is the job of scheduling and timing. A refinery under construction could be all but complete and ready to operate, but because of a delay in getting valves or heat exchangers or instruments delivered on time the entire project would be idle.

The Petroleum Administration, early in its career, set about to develop standards of efficient use which would assure the distribution of available quantities of materials equitably among the operators of the industry so as to obtain the maximum production. By way of illustration, the production branch of the industry consumes huge volumes of steel and other essential materials in the drilling of oil wells and in carrying on its production operations. The Petroleum Administration has sought to eliminate the drilling of all unnecessary wells — unnecessary purely in the sense that they would represent a relatively ineffective use of steel. This is accomplished by the issuance of regulations as to the spacing of wells. These regulations were designed to prevent the drilling of wells virtually on top of one another as too frequently had been the competitive practice. We have sought at the same time to encourage the discovery of new oil reserves by excepting from the terms of the regulations the drilling of all wildcat or exploratory wells. Provision was of course made for appropriate exceptions so that individual hard cases could be handled on a necessarily individual basis. Likewise, controls were established over the use of materials and equipment used in production operations after wells have been completed and in the various other branches of the oil industry.

There are literally hundreds of scarce items and the tremendous job of passing upon the thousands of requests and applications for materials will be readily recognized.

The program of efficient use-determination was supplemented by a technical " screening " process established in the Petroleum Administration. Every proposal or application for materials is subjected to the most searching study. We require answers to these questions — is the project essential to the war program; could any less critical material be substituted?

In cases of particular projects we have sought to establish more efficient engineering techniques.

With a view to preventing an unnecessary drain on new materials a Salvage Section was established in the Materials Division of the Petroleum Administration. This section operates both in this country and abroad. It has brought together the representatives of American companies in Latin America with the Board of Economic Warfare and this Office on a program for the return of scrap metals in Latin America to this country where they can be used. The Salvage Section has not only set up procedures for the industry, it has been successful in establishing programs with certain manufacturers, especially with those of subsurface pumps to recover parts suitable for reconditioning so as to make unnecessary the fabrication of new parts.

The Salvage Section, moreover, has developed a source of information whereby available quantities of material may be recovered from other industries for use by the petroleum industry. On several occasions it has " thawed out " frozen freight destined for areas outside of the United States which, for military or other reasons, could not be shipped. This activity is also being carried out in connection with the miscellaneous items acquired from refineries which have been sold and moved to other countries.

An inventory redistribution program has been established for the purpose of redistributing surplus stocks in the industry to individuals who can put them to immediate use. Let me illustrate: The X Company has a supply of certain essential materials which it acquired during pre-war days. The Y Company, either through lack of foresight or money, isn't so fortunate. But it has need of the very materials of which the X Company has a supply, and in this hypothetical case the Y Company was helped over the hump by the X Company. We have studied existing inventories and have endeavored to bring them into balance with war demands.

An important part of the Petroleum Administration's " doing more with less " program is the joint use of facilities. In normal times, under the laws of our land, we are expected to operate as distinct and separate entities, and to avoid scrupulously anything that savors of a combination in restraint of trade. The purpose back of the antitrust laws is, of course, to assure genuine competition. Under this system there inevitably results a considerable duplication of effort and of facilities — more in some fields than in others. Over the long run this justifies itself by the resulting improvements which spring from keen competition. But in time of such a war as this, we are faced with the necessity of taking a short-range view. We must immediately utilize to the full present capacity every resource, every facility which contributes to the success of the immediate war drive. What is ordinarily a normal duplication in other times suddenly becomes, in a world at war, an unjustifiable waste.

Through the whole-hearted cooperation of the pe-

troleum industry we have been able to show great
savings in manpower and materials through pooling
and sharing, and, generally, operating as one big industry engaged in winning a war. The savings are particularly noticeable in the marketing and distributing
branches of the industry. In certain important areas
it is believed that the physical job of distribution
could be accomplished with not more than 50 per cent
of the bulk plants normally in operation. Likewise
savings in motor transport and manpower have been
effected through consolidation.

The program for the joint use of facilities not only
releases men and materials for war service, it helps as
well to meet a financial problem of the times. Cost
reductions accomplish as much for the industry as
price advances in an equivalent amount. There is
nothing inflationary in a reduction of expenses.

The petroleum industry undoubtedly faces an extremely difficult year, one that will test it to the limit.
With essential war industries requiring an ever-
increasing volume of fuel oil, and with shipments for
military use on the fighting fronts assuming ever larger
proportions, consumption is well on the upgrade.
During the past year the increasing war requirements
have been largely offset, as we have shown, by restricted civilian demand. However, we can't go much
further in that direction because of actual hardship
and perhaps even suffering.

Faced with an increasing war demand for oil, the
industry must use its facilities with the utmost efficiency. As more millions of men are called to the

colors, the remaining reserves of manpower must be employed with an ever greater effectiveness. With oil from American fields powering British bombers over Europe, Navy fighters over the Solomons, Army planes in India, Soviet fighters from Rostov to Leningrad, General Sherman tanks in Africa, and American air forces in China, we realize that we have assumed a staggering burden.

By squeezing out the maximum efficiency from existing facilities, by making the most effective use of inventories and salvageable equipment, and by a carefully controlled use of new materials, the oil industry has managed to make hundreds of thousands of tons of steel and other critical material available for the manufacture of ships, planes, and guns, and at the same time has been able to fulfill its basic responsibility of supplying enough oil, on time.

CHAPTER SEVEN

Enemy Ersatz

For reasons that must be apparent, I shall confine the discussion of this subject to a few broad generalizations in order merely to complete the general thesis that I have in mind.

In any intelligent consideration of Hitler's oil supply we must recognize this important factor: Germany's economy, prior to the war, was not geared to the use of petroleum in anything approaching the degree that our own was.

Thus, on the one hand, the enemy has been able to get along with so little, as compared with the volume of our own requirements, that it hasn't always been easy to understand how he did it.

On the other hand, the economy of this country, highly geared as it has been to the use of oil, had the flexibility which was an indispensable element when it became necessary to convert, on short notice, to a wartime production level.

In their drives for self-sufficiency, Germany, Italy, and Japan have operated their industries to a substantial extent by the use of coal and other fuels such as alcohol, gas generated by machines, etc. Civilian consumption, such as it was in Germany and Austria at the outbreak of the war, was cut deeply, while civilian consumption in Axis Europe as a whole is estimated to have been cut even more severely.

The war caught Hitler in the middle of his program to promote his much vaunted *Autobahnen* — 1,800 miles of it were completed by the end of 1938. Incidentally he had promised all good Germans a *Volkswagen,* a popular-priced automobile, which they paid for in advance but never got.

Generally speaking, however, the dislocations confronting the enemy on his home front at the start of hostilities were only relative, and not as violent as those which were bound to occur in an economic system that had become dependent on oil. In the final analysis Hitler found himself with the greater part of his entire oil supply available for military uses.

The enemy has found that ersatz fuels require huge drains on critical materials as well as on manpower, and that it takes time to build up the productive capacity. We have been discovering at the same time that large supplies of oil give an element of mobility and flexibility that would otherwise be totally lacking.

Imagine, if you can, what a railroad bottleneck we would have if our principal source of fuel for home, industry, farm, mine, and power plant were coal which had to be transported thousands of miles back and forth across the continent!

Imagine, if you can, the effect on our transportation facilities if hundreds of thousands of our workers were without their own independent means of travel!

Imagine, if you can, how severely our war program would have bogged down if we had had to allocate huge volumes of steel and equipment, plus manpower, to produce, synthetically, the oil itself! As it was we had a substantial reserve capacity to meet the expanding war requirements.

We were fortunate in having this reserve productive capacity at the outbreak of the war, but having it was not a matter of luck. Instead, it was the well-deserved and highly important dividend paid to us for ten years of concerted effort by State and Federal officials and the technologists and managers of the oil industry in eliminating physical waste and improving the engineering practices used in the production of oil and gas. While Hitler was building a war machine, we were learning how to safeguard our oil supply.

That Germany has never been geared in the degree that we have to the use of oil gives us reason to suspect that Hitler can continue to get along with what he has, much less than our own though it be, and that it will see him, in a nerve-racking sort of a way, through a long war.

If this comes as a shock to the optimists who have been expecting Hitler to run short almost any day, blame it on the military experts of the newspaper

offices. Haven't they been insisting ever since 1938
that another season would see Hitler's finish? The edi-
torial strategists at first promised us faithfully that the
Nazi machine would stall and come to a stop not later
than the spring of 1941, all for want of gasoline. When
that deadline passed without anything happening, it
was explained that "Fury" had probably acquired
enough petroleum from his subjugated neighbors to
keep him going until the winter of 1941–42, but not
a day longer. The winter came and went and the Nazi
murder machine kept right on rolling. It didn't slow
down. Neither did the kindergarten forecasters who,
without attempting to explain the delay in the fulfill-
ment of their prognostications, gave Hitler until the
summer of 1942 to run out of gasoline.

Here we are well into 1943 and there is no easily
visible sign that the end is in sight, at least for the reason that Hitler's petroleum supply is exhausted. We
hear encouraging reports, however, from what may be
considered reliable sources, that the European Axis
oil supply as of January last was at an uncomfortable
low.

I think that we have already wasted precious time
waiting for Hitler's military collapse for lack of petroleum, and my earnest suggestion is that we let the military take its course and that we continue to carry on
with our rat-killing. If the Nazis should by any chance
run out of gasoline, they would be just that much easier to lick. If they don't, we will have wasted a minimum of time watching anxiously for Hitler's tank
gauge to show "Empty."

It is no idle boast to say that if the winner in a finish fight such as this one is between the United Nations and the Axis partners were to be chosen on the basis of oil alone, it wouldn't be Hitler and his gang. We know that, and yet the most encouraging thing that may be said at this writing is that we *hope* that Hitler's cruse of oil is as low as the experts have been telling us for two years that it should be — and with no Elijah to help him. If we were to get any real comfort out of such wishfulness it would be necessary for us to overlook the well-known fact that Germany has been working incessantly since the last world debacle to perfect and to increase the production of synthetic gasoline by hydrogenation processes and related methods of processing coals, lignites, tars, etc. We would have to ignore the extent of Germany's coal deposits in the Ruhr Valley; the ingenuity and the cunning of Germany's scientists; and the fiendishness with which the lustful Nazis are draining the limited oil fields of the conquered countries. However, these are things that we cannot discount easily if we are to be realistic.

Our attitude toward the war would be more sensible if we disabused our minds of the popular notions to which we have been clinging concerning the Nazi oil supply. Until we actually see it give out we will be ahead of the game if we chart our course on the stern assumption of what it seems to be, and not on what we hope it is, or even on what some say that it should be.

We took it entirely too much for granted, I am convinced, that Germany attacked Russia out of a desperate need for oil that she thought — very mistakenly as it turned out — was to be had in the Soviet Republic for the taking. We somehow couldn't account for Hitler's folly on any other ground. When the Reds thrust the mad Nazis back on their heels, and launched the most amazing counter-offensive in all history, we cheered lustily, believing that Germany's failure to reach the Caucasus or the Grozny or the Baku areas meant inevitable ruin, and probably an early crack-up of the Nazi machine. We rejoiced that Germany had played its last desperate high card and lost. But there is still no sign of a crack-up.

I am inclined to fall into step with Premier Stalin when he says that what Germany really aimed to do was to outflank Moscow and cut it off from the Volga and the Russian rear in the Urals rather than to augment its own oil supply. Stalin's analysis of the German drive was that the loss of its oil fields would have been of more immediate hurt to Russia than of help to Germany. Germany did capture Maikop, which represented about 7 per cent of Russia's total oil production, or in the neighborhood of 17,000,000 barrels a year, and has since lost it back to the amazing Red Army. It has been said that during its brief tenancy Germany was unable to extract any significant amounts of oil from Maikop.

No doubt many well-intentioned conclusions were based on the very desperateness of the Nazi drive toward the Caucasus. I wish that I could bring myself to believe that failure to reach the Caucasus would prove to be a major Nazi catastrophe.

Let no one suppose that I think for one minute that

the Nazis don't want or couldn't make use of Russia's oil, or that they would not still be willing to pay a big price for it in equipment and in their rapidly thinning Aryan blood. I am merely trying to give emphasis to my opinion that there is a real danger in hanging the motive that prompted Germany's attack on Russia on what we have been surmising was her need for oil. German reverses in the Caucasus and areas thereabout, if measured by that, might give us a feeling of smugness so far as our own petroleum situation is concerned that wouldn't be too good for us.

Rommel's Nazi army was supposed to be unbeatable, and so it seemed to be until it ran short of gasoline. But just what did it prove? Not that the Germans didn't have the gasoline to ship to Rommel, but that they couldn't get it to him. Axis tanker after tanker went to the bottom while attempting to reach port with petroleum for Rommel. The Rommelians had to take to their heels when they had no more oil to carry them forward.

Another possible reason for Hitler's failure to get oil to Rommel is that the Fuehrer's railroad transportation system appears to have been breaking down fast. The RAF hasn't helped Hitler even a little bit with its bombings of western Germany where a big part of Nazi shipping originates.

Dr. Gustav Stolper, once a member of the *Reichstag* committee dealing with railroads, but now a full-blown American citizen, recently told the Academy of Political Science that since the fall of France the

German railroad organization has been adapted to the flow of material and men to the east.

"It is hard to imagine how Germany can prevent a breakdown of that overstrained system," said Dr. Stolper, "when an attack in the west and south forces her to reverse the direction of that entire traffic. The reserves that enabled Germany in 1941 to start its abortive campaign in Russia, and that obviously strangled the German strength in the second offensive against Russia in 1942, do not exist any longer. In this, as in so many other respects, Hitler has reached the end of his rope."

German railroads, according to Dr. Stolper, have fallen behind in the race with transportation requirements. The *Reichsbahn* should have produced 700 locomotives annually, but the actual yearly average of locomotives delivered during the thirties was between 100 and 200. On top of this the RAF has been concentrating on locomotives to such an extent that the *Reichsbahn* now equips its engines with anti-aircraft guns. Even with these, the losses have been reduced only slightly.

"Transportation shortages," said Dr. Stolper, "will properly be described as the first and paramount weakness which led to their (the totalitarian criminals') destruction."

So it seems reasonable that, in addition to the failure of Nazi tankers to reach port with petroleum for Rommel, the railroads, which, Hitler now undoubtedly regrets, were his step-children, may have blown up in the Fuehrer's face.

There is a recent report from Stockholm that Hitler has transferred all non-war freight to canals and that all mail to the front has been stopped because of the transportation shortage. Although notoriously short of railroad engines, the Nazis apparently feel that heavy guns and armament are more important since one of their big engine repair shops has been converted to the production of heavy arms.

It is one of the theories built up about the fate of the French Toulon fleet that it was unable to get away because its oil tanks were dry. Perhaps the oil tanks were drained so that the fleet would lose its mobility. Whatever the true story is, we cannot say with any certainty that the Germans couldn't have fueled the fleet had they been given the right kind of friendly cooperation, or had they been able to get shipments through in the first instance.

To sum it all up, what I am getting at is that I think Germany could scare up the necessary oil but not the means to ship it freely. I believe that this is the true answer to Rommel's role of hare to the Allied Armies' hounds.

Within the past 25 years Germany has developed a very large plant capacity for the treatment of bituminous coals, lignites, and coal tars, and the gasoline that it has been getting from such treatment is giving, we are told, generally satisfactory results. As a matter of fact, there has been current a rumor that Germany is now producing a synthetic gasoline that is superior to our own high-octane gasoline. Whatever the truth of this report, I am confident that our present and prospective production capacity of high-octane gasoline will be in excess of that of all three of the Axis powers.

In addition to its synthetic gasoline supply, Germany relies heavily upon the use of substitute fuels and lubricants. Prominent in this category are the alcohols, " bottled " gases, and gas produced by self-contained generators. Artificial gas and even sewer gas are likewise being compressed and used for mobile equipment as well as in stationary engines. Although these substitute fuels are limited in their direct military uses in Germany, they are nevertheless playing an important role in supplying civilian and defense needs at home and so releasing more valuable motor power to Hitler's armies.

Synthetic lubricants have also been highly developed in Germany. These are being derived from various vegetable sources — seeds, nuts, resins, etc. — and from the processing of waxes. Even before the war, the synthetic lubricant industry had been carefully built up and it can be presumed that such lubricants are now being used in Germany's aviation motors to a considerable extent.

The grand total of oil available for Axis use may not be very impressive when compared to our own production of about 4 million barrels every day. We must not, however, let such a comparison give rise to false hopes or give us big ideas. We should never lose sight of the fact that Hitler hasn't the domestic demand that we have by many millions of barrels. Moreover, we must transport petroleum products to our fighters over distances varying from 3,000 to 10,000 miles, each mile attended by many hazards, while Hitler is working at relatively close range and in comparative immunity from attack.

Although its natural crude supply may be limited, there is no apparent limit to the amount of liquid fuels and lubricants that Germany could produce synthetically, or to the quantity of substitutes that are available to it. The only really serious limitation is the ability to find the manpower and the materials, particularly steel, for the construction and the operation of the plants and other facilities required for full production. It takes several times more in labor and materials to produce synthetic fuels for motors than it does to refine from natural crudes. And so we are entitled to entertain reasonable encouragement from the fact that Germany's ready yield of synthetics and substitutes does have such definite practical limitations which shortages in labor and materials may impose, and there is no harm in hoping, within reason, that she may already be strained to meet crowding requirements. But that bit of daydreaming should go hand-in-hand with the sobering realization that we, too, are facing problems of shortages with respect to both men and materials.

When shells fell on Pearl Harbor, the Japs are believed by oil men to have accumulated at least a two-years' peacetime storage supply of gasoline which would be equivalent to a 15-months' *wartime* supply.

All estimates of Japan's storage supply of gasoline at the outbreak of hostilities were based strictly on its needs for military purposes. For nearly five years prior to Pearl Harbor, Japan regulated the use of oil by its civilian population, always having in mind, even while giving noisy and lying lip service to the cause of peace, that some day it was going to be at war with the United States. Only a few months before Pearl Harbor the sale of gasoline for pleasure driving in Japan was prohibited. Taxicabs were ordered off of the streets when, in July 1941, the Netherlands and the United States at long last put a stop to the exportation of oil to the island. While hoarding and hiding the gasoline with which we had supplied them, and which they were to use against us when we weren't looking, the Japs, up to December 7, 1941, were seldom, if ever, stymied in their hunt for information about our petroleum situation.

Since 1935, the Bureau of Mines, in the Department of the Interior, has regularly advertised the activities of the Japanese in the construction of laboratories and plants for the conversion of the lignite reserves of Japan, Korea, and Manchuria. We should have taken our cue from that if from nothing else, and gone on the instant alert. We watched the wily Japs as they adopted Germany's scientific processes for the production of synthetic gasoline, for the production of rubber, and of explosives. In Japan's discovery of unlimited coal reserves that could be made to wet-nurse a hungry war machine, the Japanese dream of destroying America was born. We suspected all of that, and even discussed it frankly in public forums. Information in support of our suspicions was given wide publicity, but so naive and unsuspecting had America always been in its dealings with other nations that to very few did the evil intentions of the Japs occur. Even while we knew what Japan was doing, and the warlike preparations that she was making, we were adding constantly and cheerfully to her storehouse of knowledge, and to her fighting equipment by regular shipments of petroleum, petroleum products, and scrap iron.

Japan, as in the case of Germany, worked up a substantial synthetic oil production. Japan is now supposed to have found a way to make gasoline out of rubber, but I wouldn't worry too much about that since it would require great quantities of critical materials, which Japan does not have to spare, to construct the necessary facilities if any worthwhile results were to be achieved. Some of our most conservative newspapers have become greatly agitated over the report that Japan has a plant already in operation in Malaya where, it is said, it will turn out 100 tons of high-octane gasoline a month when it reaches full capacity. This is equivalent to approximately 25 barrels a day. One bomber would use that up in less than eight hours! Speculation that Japan might eventually use all of the 1,200,000 tons of rubber that it can obtain in a year from the Far East and turn it into 900,000 tons of gasoline and fuel oil is, in my opinion, something else not to worry about. I would say that if Japan lives to see the day that it will be getting such a production for the present emergency, we are in for a much longer war than even I figure that we are.

Japan has small oil fields on the Island of Honshu;

also on the Island of Hokkaido to the north. Another source of indigenous production available to Japan is on the Island of Formosa. In 1941, the last year for which reasonably accurate figures are available, Japan's total production of crude oil from these sources amounted to 2,657,000 barrels, or about 7,300 barrels daily.

In addition to these sources, Japan gets some of its oil from the northern half of Sakhalin Island which is Russia-controlled. There is no significant oil production from the southern half which is Japan's. Japan has long had a concession arrangement with Russia which gives her the privilege of operating anywhere in Sakhalin and withdrawing crude. There is little available information either as to the nature of the arrangement, or the amount of oil that Japan derives under it.

Over a number of years prior to the war, as I have already said, Japan's policy, according to some well-informed oil men, was to keep in constant supply a two years' storage of petroleum products and crude oil. Japan's estimate of what this supply should represent in actual barrels of products for war was based no doubt upon her own secret determination to fight it out with the United States and England and the Netherlands whenever she felt that the time was ripe, and her extreme confidence that, with the aid of her gods, goddesses, and long-dead ancestors she could lick all three of us when that time came. She must have estimated, on the occasion of Pearl Harbor, that her storage supply assured her of a petroleum competence for two years even against the combined strength of the three opposing nations, and not counting what she would have to use against China if she were to continue the hammering which she has been inflicting without conclusive results for six years. Since Pearl Harbor, Japan has captured some petroleum supplies in countries that, like Germany, she has overrun. In addition to these she took possession of some oil fields and refineries in the Dutch East Indies before they could be completely wrecked. In all cases the Japs are believed to have moved in fast enough with drilling machinery, casings, and drill pipes to have started the work of restoration with a minimum loss of time.

Prior to the war Japan's main reliance, next to what she could import, mainly by the grace of Britain and the United States, was upon a hydrocarbon synthesis, shale oil production in Manchuria, and about 8,000 barrels a day of well production. Since then the Nazis must have shared with Japan their own development of synthetic processes.

As I have intimated, speculation as to the enemy's petroleum assets is bound to be more or less unconvincing. The other side of it is that the enemy is similarly handicapped when he attempts to weigh our own case, with this qualification, namely, that he seems to have been able to get more information from us than we have from him. In addition to being more direct, the data he picks up concerning our petroleum are generally more recent than our information about his. I have tried to be liberal in my opinion of the enemy's strength on the theory that if he is not that

strong so much the better. It is much safer to err on the
side of overstatement in such matters. If we knew ac-
curately what petroleum products the enemy has to
burn, we could more closely guess as to his air strength,
to say nothing of the tanks and subs that he has been
able to throw into the fight.

Let us not lose sight of the one basic probability,
however, that the enemy isn't going to be overcome
by technical surveys any more than we are going to
win the war, to quote a radio wit, " with arm bands."
What the enemy has to fight with, be it much or little,
will be used to the limit against our sons and brothers,
and we should never make the guilty mistake of under-
estimating it.

I cannot contemplate the future without conjuring
up a vision of the day when the Allied armies will
actually invade Europe and Japan. Of course we know
that such an invasion will be a terrific shock to the
Nazi and Japanazi economic systems. We do not know
what complications and ramifications will thus be
added to our own petroleum perplexities. Not even
an Elijah would find it easy to announce this authori-
tatively in advance. The very thought of it sometimes
makes me wonder if we have seen anything yet in fuel
oil restrictions and sacrifices here at home. Our hauls
will conceivably be longer when the invasions take
place; and hazards en route will almost certainly be
increased, and consequently more and greater readjustments will be found necessary right here on American soil.

But after discounting what we think that we know

about Germany's and Japan's oil problems, and knowing what we do about our own (much of which we are not at liberty to divulge) we are still able to say that, in this great Battle of Oil, we — the United Nations — remain top-heavy favorites to win.

CHAPTER EIGHT

Fightin' Oil and Modern Alchemy

A few weeks ago I heard this question propounded to Mr. Geoffrey Lloyd, M.P., Great Britain's Petroleum Secretary:

"Do you think 100-octane was the deciding factor in the Battle of Britain back in 1940?"

To which Mr. Lloyd shot back the quick reply:

"I think we wouldn't have won the Battle of Britain without 100-octane — but we *did* have the 100-octane."

There was a note of triumph in Mr. Lloyd's voice, and why not?

As England might not have won the Battle of Britain without 100-octane gasoline, so the United Nations might not today be getting the upper hand in their fight with the Germans and the Japs were it not for the greater supply of superfuel which gives our fighter planes the speed, power, and maneuverability that will spell ultimate and certain victory in the air.

In addition to the military and essential civilian needs for regular petroleum products, there have developed increasing demands for three petroleum synthetics — 100-octane aviation gasoline, toluene for explosives, and raw materials for synthetic rubber. The astronomical requirements of our air force for aviation gasoline today take me back two short years when it was no military secret that we were dangerously short of capacity for making it. Our ability to produce at that time out of the plants then built and those about to be completed was estimated at about 40,000 barrels a day, and 1,000 two-engine bombers, each burning 5.5 barrels an hour, would, we knew, lick that up in 7.3 hours. On a 400-mile raid into Europe from England, 1,000 two-engine bombers were estimated to burn approximately 925,000 gallons, or a little more than 22,000 barrels, of aviation fuel. It all made our capacity for making it look pretty thin and sickly.

Frankly, I was tremendously worried. As I looked over the situation, I was — I am now free to confess — extremely dubious of our chances for getting production to a level that would be anywhere nearly adequate. The first difficulty was that there were only about a dozen refiners in the country who even knew how to make 100-octane. The second was that the steel, copper, and other materials, required for new refinery facilities, were scarce — critically scarce. The third difficulty was that refinery engineers estimated that it would take from a year to 18 months to build the required new units — and who was there to guarantee that we would be safe from invasion for as long as 18 months?

But whatever the nature or the number of the difficulties confronting us, it was clear to those of us who regarded the country's prospects for continued peace with no little pessimism, that something had to be done, and quickly.

So, in the summer of 1941, I told the representatives of the petroleum industry that we must start immediately on a program to double our 100-octane capacity. Obviously, that was a big assignment in any man's world. It meant the expenditure of many millions of dollars. Added to the fact that the oil industry and I hadn't yet gone away on our "honeymoon," the suggestion, generally speaking, was not well received for both economic and personal reasons. After all, the country was at peace, and many persons still clung to the hope that we might remain so. Why, then, did we need all of that high-octane gasoline?

But, as I believe quite a few people may have heard, I am a persistent person. Some people have a stronger word for it. The oil men yielded to my importunings and the gigantic job was undertaken. Thereupon, I revised my estimates and insisted that, instead of merely doubling our 100-octane capacity, we should treble it. In fact, so hard am I to satisfy, that, before

Pearl Harbor, we were shooting at a goal of 150,000 barrels a day, nearly four times the production when the subject first came up; and though exact figures are now a military secret, I can assure you that the 150,000 figure has long since been obsolete.

I wish that I might make public the present production figures of 100-octane. (Even the " 100-octane standard of measurement " is getting a little old-fashioned, because fuels are improving in qualities which are not measured on the octane scale.) It represents a near miracle, the proportions of which cannot, unfortunately, be appreciated by anyone who does not understand the intricacies of the refinery equipment which is necessary, and the complexity of the processes involved. It has been achieved because we have had a smoothly functioning Government-Industry partnership; because the holders of patents on complicated processes, which had been worked out through years of experimentation and at huge expense, agreed to make those processes available at sharply reduced royalties to all who would participate in the effort; because the experts of our Office and those of the industry worked wonders in improving processes, and in devising ways to avoid the use of scarce materials; because rival companies were willing to share with one another their raw materials, their knowledge, and their facilities — because, in brief, there was a will to do, and the organization with which to do it.

The construction of new refining units went forward in spite of the difficulty of building new units.

The really spectacular part of it was the accomplishments with the facilities that were in existence at the time. The output was soon more than 50 per cent greater than anyone had even dreamed of when the war began. This is the 100-octane gasoline which has been created by the sheer wizardry of America's technical men. It is this gasoline that made possible the victories of the Coral Sea and Midway and more recently of the Bismarck Sea; the gasoline that carried Jimmy Doolittle and his armada over Tokyo; the gasoline that will take more and bigger armadas over Tokyo — and Berlin and Rome; the gasoline that made it possible for us to smack down the ears of Rommel in North Africa and which caused a United States Army General to remark to one of my staff members:

" The job which has been done with 100-octane by the refinery experts of your staff and of the oil industry is one of the most amazing things I have ever witnessed. It is almost unbelievable. They have virtually squeezed it out of a hat."

Today we are producing the major part of the world's aviation gasoline (it may even run as high as 95 per cent of it — nothing would surprise me greatly after what I have seen the petroleum industry do!), and the volume of our production is rising steadily.

When I said that even 100-octane gasoline is beginning to be a little old-fashioned, I was probably thinking more particularly of the catalytic cracking plants that are now opening up in many parts of the country with startling regularity. They come close, in my opinion, to being the last nail in the coffin of the Axis. The new superfuel that they produce has quality factors which make it even better than the 100-octane of a year ago, and the use of it gives the American-made plane the advantage of greatly superior speed and maneuverability. Fueled with it, one of our bombers can carry a 25 per cent greater bomb load. In other words, on a long-range offensive to the Axis capitals, 1,000 American-made four-engine bombers with an aggregate bomb capacity of 8,000,000 pounds would be able to transport 2,000,000 more pounds of explosives on every visit than if fueled with yesterday's 100-octane gasoline. A two-engine bomber with a 4,000-pound bomb capacity can carry another 1,000 pounds. And that, as someone has observed, " ain't feathers."

All together, some 16 American companies are now producing aviation gasoline of this superlative grade. One of them has said that it is alone making 60 times as much of it as it did two years ago. When the plants now being constructed are finished, 20 large American companies will be producing superfuel, and 35 smaller refining companies will have key parts in the program. These 55 companies are being " backstopped " by a large number of other refining companies and natural gasoline companies which provide precious ingredients of 100-octane that contribute to the national productive capacity. (That noise you hear is *not* the Reichsfuehrer nor il Duce cheering!) Our fighting planes have been especially designed to burn this superfuel which, if it could be burned in a standard motor car, would drive it 40 miles on one gallon. The Axis did not have the natural resources or the manufacturing equipment which would permit it to plan its aircraft engines to use the superfuel on which our military program is based.

Although we still refer to it as "aviation gasoline," actually it isn't gasoline at all, but a superfuel that is produced by rearranging the petroleum hydrocarbon molecules through the use of catalysts.

A catalyst is described as "any substance which, solely by its presence, permits the acceleration of chemical reaction, between two or more other chemicals." Just as the preacher marries but does not marry himself, the catalyst transforms but never mixes. That is why it might be called the "petroleum parson."

Catalytic cracking is explained as "splitting, or reforming, a crude oil distillate into a number of new and lighter compounds in the presence of a catalyst."

These catalytic processes will, among other things, (1) make synthetically from petroleum a basically better and more powerful fuel, (2) remove the natural impurities which, in motor cars, are only nuisances, but which, in airplanes, may mean the loss of human life, and, (3) produce other petroleum derivatives, some of which become blending agents to get the highest octane ratings, while others go into various synthetic products. One of the most important of these synthetic products is rubber.

It may startle you to learn, as it did me, that before the end of 1943 the United States will produce a quarter of a million tons of synthetic rubber, and nearly

一九四一年十月仲日

某某先生

稅老羕哀仙妃　WHEAT, POTATOES, STRING BEANS AND GARLIC

后員契與求　HOUDRY PROCESS　前後商慣名幽巅霜脂贇　靜

罷耒丰之　豐契襤賀　覀丫氺氺丫丫　厇專冪冪　縱出

STANDARD OIL COMPANY OF NEW JERSEY　假嘆刷古　DEMOCRATIC PARTY　螢夢

爲釋景玨　緊身糞築嘸蘇　寽心功少華　艍艍人王丰

槊館　IN A BATH TUB　舌搜安流蔣願思扶　冡騆觝寙爲容

綠圖白緋會仁者者若　JESSE JONES　氜口身廾　新蚈蓬糸

GIRDLES　聞發轉寫　覓會重覓　身配洞村　雒夫呼名歐

伍仰放作知　THREE CUPS OF SUGAR　出將肄圖慚　擺彡　干雜

FRANK PHILLIPS　柴本能相情雒印覓施景　酒許私桃杏女

轉覿　房輕　聲會後雪　北

光月仙竘

I haven't submitted this "Synthetic Rubber Report" to the critical eye of a student of Chinese so that I can't very well vouch for what it says. As a matter of fact, I wouldn't want to bet too much that the characters are all Chinese. This "report" has been floating about the Nation's capital for some little time, which leads me to assume with a reasonable degree of confidence that if there had been anything improper or dangerous about it we would have heard of it ere this.

four times that amount in 1944. This is the published expectation of the Rubber Administration. Synthetic rubber is based in large part on petroleum raw materials. In addition to that the Petroleum Administrator has a direct responsibility in the rubber program under the President's order. Hence my very deep interest in it.

A million tons of rubber was virtually the entire world consumption in a pre-war year. A half a million tons is almost as much as the United States has ever used in a normal year; it is also nearly as much as our estimated military, essential civilian, and United Nations export demands, exclusive of passenger car tires, for 1943. The anticipated output for 1944 is expected to meet all essential needs, and allow for the necessary building up of inventories.

One of the really amazing stories of ersatz production that will have to wait for peace before it can be told concerns toluene, the basic element in TNT, the deadly explosive that will eventually blast the enemy into unconditional surrender. During the first World War the petroleum industry manufactured some toluene, but in the period between the wars it bowed out of that field in favor of the coal distillation industry. Until shortly before Pearl Harbor the entire national production came as a by-product from the operation of coke ovens. Such production has just about reached its peak, and in no case can it be substantially increased. At its best this by-product output would not have been anywhere nearly enough to meet present military needs.

When war was declared the petroleum industry fairly leaped into the production of toluene and already is making $2\frac{1}{2}$ times as much of it as is produced from all other sources. By the end of the current year, the production of toluene from petroleum will be more than doubled, and will be nearly 6 times the volume produced from all by-product operations.

The case of toluene offers another striking example of the speed with which a country geared to the use of oil is able to adapt itself to any emergency in which petroleum plays a part. We are still short of our toluene requirements, but on the basis of present expansion it shouldn't be long before we catch up with our military demands.

And there you have a pastoral scene of a peace-loving people — American-made bombers, powered by superfuel, and loaded with TNT!

What peace will bring us in the way of petroleum-based goods is a subject that only a chemist is qualified to discuss. In the chemical world it is stated that the commodities to come from petroleum will overshadow, in curious interest at least, the products which it now gives us. Soaps, dyes, wearing apparel, and even foods, are in prospect.

When we consider how valuable and versatile petroleum is and the increasingly important part that it is destined to play during the years ahead, I am sure that there will be a more unanimous and whole-hearted acceptance of measures designed to conserve and use wisely this irreplaceable natural resource.

CHAPTER NINE

Oil in the
Ground

Until recently there was a disposition on the part of the public to take it as a matter of course that there was as much oil in the ground as there was water. We burned it on that basis. In fact we have been shamefully extravagant of it.

Frankly, the oil industry is itself largely responsible for this public attitude. "By the mere opening of valves we could overnight add 30 per cent to our production," oil companies used to advertise boastfully. As recently as two years ago they were assuring us that they could meet any probable requirement that even a world war might thrust upon them. I have never questioned the honesty or good faith back of their statements.

While the discovery of oil resources had been up and down, the industry had usually managed to find enough new fields to make up for withdrawals. Every so often someone would get the jitters and warn of a crude shortage. This would invariably be followed by the discovery of tremendous new reserves.

Soon after the last war the U. S. Geological Survey of the Department of the Interior sounded off an alarm, and the ink was no more than dry on it before an incredible amount of oil was found and opened up. Naturally the public decided, on the basis of these experiences, that an oil shortage in the United States, after all was said and done, was an impossibility.

The industry itself was under an illusion because it overrated its ability to produce. After ten years of production under pro-ration, estimated "potentials" had been built up in some areas to fantastic and unreal figures.

Of course no one ever anticipated the kind of a war that the world has worked up to. The most imaginative oil man couldn't possibly have conceived the magnitude of the demands that were to be made upon the industry; nor could he have known in advance the severity of the restrictions under which the industry would have to operate because of the limited available supplies of steel and other materials. The reaction that would result from the disruption of the tanker service he never could have guessed. In short, the war confronted the petroleum industry with a problem for which there was no precedent; nor anything approaching one.

Although the oil men of the country soon realized after the start of hostilities how far wrong they had been, the public, lacking the knowledge of the oil men, wasn't so quick to revise its estimate of our petroleum supply situation. Its accepted belief was that it would never run out. To this day some Government administrators carry about the idea, based on what the industry itself asked them no longer than two years ago to take for granted, that our petroleum supply has no bottom.

One unfortunate result of this is that the production branch of the industry has great difficulty in obtaining essential supplies. The conviction that " by the mere opening of valves " petroleum production could be increased 30 per cent overnight will not down and persists in many unexpected quarters. So strong is it on occasion that suggestions have been made to the industry to take a holiday from drilling operations in order to make critical materials available for other urgent needs. Elsewhere I have attempted to show that this threatens a critical situation.

The truth is that since 1939 oil has not been discovered fast enough to replace that which we have produced and consumed, and at the same time to maintain our reserves in balance. On January 1, 1943, conservative estimates placed proven crude oil reserves of the Nation at about 20 billion barrels. In terms of 1942 consumption, this would represent approximately a 14 years' supply if it could be produced as needed. The nature of oil reserves is such, however, that the oil in the reserves cannot be produced at will. Productive capacities decline as the fields are exploited and the reservoir energy depleted.

As many as 20 to 40 years will be required to obtain the oil remaining in many of the reservoirs today.

Without the discovery of new reserves in quantities that are at least equal to the rate at which crude oil is being produced and consumed, the country's productive capacity must and will decline.

Why, someone asks, should we be concerned with the development of still greater capacity to produce when we actually have additional productive capacity in some producing areas which can find no outlet? The answer is that most of this excess capacity is not available because of transportation limitations. The transportation problems will have to be solved to an even greater degree than at present if we are to avail ourselves of our full productive capacity, and in certain areas we will probably face actual shortages in the near future. Looking ahead only two short years we can see a decidedly disturbing production problem. Beyond that the future is not predictable with any confidence.

Moreover, there is no reason to believe that demand will remain at its present level. There is a lot of support for the opinion that the future petroleum requirement for war — direct and indirect — will increase substantially. Thus far restrictions upon the non-war uses of petroleum have to a great extent offset the added war demand, but this is not likely to be a continuing experience.

In the United States we have already explored intensively our potential oil-producing areas. It therefore seems obvious that we have consumed a greater portion of our total reserves than have other oil-producing countries. There is no denying the possibility — in fact, the probability — that in future years the United States may have to yield its position as the number one oil producer of the world. Our most likely successors are the Near East and Russia.

Naturally, we cannot speak about undiscovered reserves with the same assurance that we can of estimated proven reserves. Given adequate geological and engineering data, it is possible to make a fairly good estimate as to the impregnated area and measure the number of barrels to be found there. In any well-developed oil field we can obtain sufficiently reliable information on the basis of known geological conditions, the physical characteristics, depth, and extent of the productive formation, to make a fairly accurate guess as to what we can count upon in the way of future production. In areas outside of the United States the problem is complicated by factors such as political secrecy and the consequent lack of engineering data.

At a rough guess, the proven oil reserves of the world, including the United States, might be estimated at approximately 55 billion barrels. It should be realized, however, that there are many regions throughout the world that have not been explored for oil to any great extent, and we may be sure that the eventual drilling in such areas will prove up huge amounts of petroleum. For example, the oil-producing areas in the Near East have by no means been explored thoroughly, but a casual analysis of the geological structures and a comparison with the results obtained in areas already drilled enable us to be quite certain that substantial unknown reserves underlie this sun-baked portion of the earth. Likewise, there are extensive regions throughout Russia that are undeveloped.

As striking evidence of the intensity with which oil exploration has been carried on in the United States in contrast to the rest of the world, I call attention to the following comparison: It is estimated that in this country one exploratory well has been drilled for every 12 square miles of possible oil-bearing land, whereas in all other countries one exploratory well has been drilled for every 1,280 square miles of potential oil land. In other words, the search for oil has been 100 times greater in this country than elsewhere — and consequently the opportunities for new discoveries have been correspondingly reduced.

If we now turn to production, i.e., the extraction of petroleum from the ground, we find that the United States is withdrawing its petroleum at a more rapid rate than the rest of the world. In the year 1940, approximately 2,146,000,000 barrels of petroleum were pumped out of the ground throughout the world. Of this amount the United States produced 1,351,847,-000 barrels, or in the neighborhood of 63 per cent of the entire world production. It is apparent from these figures that we are using up our reserves faster than any other country. Since our whole economic system is geared to the use of huge quantities of oil, it seems clear that we will have to continue this heavy drain on our reserves — and this without the bright prospect that other countries have of replenishing a diminishing supply.

The problem of assuring adequate supplies of oil for the future is, of course, occupying the serious thought of the Government and of the petroleum industry. The exploration for new oil fields is being stimulated. During the past three years we drilled in this country about 3,116 wildcat wells per year, and discovered an average of 541,000,000 barrels of new reserves. In the previous three years fewer wildcats were drilled by 22 per cent, and yet nearly three times more oil was discovered. Although it would seem that petroleum's bonanza days are a thing of the past in this country, encouragement is being given to wildcat operations by means of preferred treatment in securing the necessary critical materials. In this and in other ways, it is hoped to offset declining reserves by new discoveries.

I have recently called upon the industry to drill a minimum of 4,500 wildcat wells during 1943. This number is 50 per cent more than the number of wildcats ever drilled in any single year. Since 1938 the discovery of new crude oil reserves has not equalled the volume of crude oil consumed. This is a condition that we cannot allow to continue indefinitely if we expect to avoid a serious shortage within a relatively short time. In other words, we must keep digging to find as near a billion and a quarter barrels of new oil each year as possible.

Discoveries of petroleum during 1942, to give you an example, did not exceed 421 million barrels on the basis of the traditional conservative methods of estimating proven crude oil reserves. If we stick to that pace it is not hard to foresee where it will land us.

We were fortunate in having a substantial backlog of crude oil reserves at the outset of the war. But the paucity of new *big* discoveries, coupled with the increasing essential demands for petroleum, is resulting in a continual drain on our accumulated crude oil reserve at a time when the outlook is for even greater essential petroleum requirements.

The cheapest and most effective way of adding a barrel of oil to our reserves is through the adoption of sound conservation principles which greatly contribute to ultimate recovery. Through the control of gas-oil ratios, the injection of gas into the producing formation, unit operations, etc., we are doing all that we can to increase the recovery from known fields.

Last fall we obtained approval of the first unit of a salt water disposal and pressure maintenance project designed to recover from 200,000,000 to 800,000,000 barrels of crude petroleum from the important East Texas field that would otherwise be lost. Moreover, it will provide for an efficient productive capacity of 400,000 barrels of oil daily from the field. Without this program the efficient capacity would be smaller by the amount of water being produced and reinjected. The project is part of a comprehensive program undertaken by the East Texas Salt Water Disposal Company costing about $500,000 and representing approximately one-quarter of the total program. A large part of the equipment that is being used is second-hand. Work is almost completed on the initial project and approval has been obtained for the second quarter of the enterprise.

Secondary recovery operations are being employed on a far wider scale than ever, as in certain Pennsylvania fields. The volume of oil ultimately recoverable cannot, of course, be measured except in terms of price. As the price of oil rises, not only will marginal wells remain in production that would otherwise have to be abandoned, but also it will be possible to engage in more expensive methods of secondary recovery and, perhaps, oil mining. Eventually, when the price of oil rises sufficiently high to offset the costs involved, it will become practical to recover oil from the vast deposits of oil shale in the western States, and to manufacture oil from coal, lignite, and other carbonaceous material.

Most of the oil-producing States have adopted sound conservation laws which are designed to regulate oil production without waste. The Petroleum Administration has collaborated with the regulatory authorities in these states to the end that the production of the crudes most needed — reckoned in terms of their value in the making of high-octane gasoline, toluol, and fuel oil — will be encouraged and stimulated, while those not so immediately important to our war program will be retained safely in their natural underground storage. Each month we certify to each of the oil-producing States recommended production rates which are designed to accomplish these objectives and to take into account the crude reserve position as well as the transportation facilities that are available to transport the crude to points where it is needed.

California is one of the important oil-producing areas that has no oil conservation statute. And it isn't because I haven't done everything within my own limited power to have such a statute enacted. California is most important in the war program because the oil requirements for the fight in the Pacific are drawn largely from it. The Army, the Navy, and defense industries are also very active in that area, and all of them use vast quantities of petroleum. California is so separated geographically from other oil-producing areas that it stands pretty much alone. There are, for instance, no pipe lines or other practical overland oil transportation facilities linking California with the Midcontinent or Gulf areas.

If it had had the foresight to adopt a sound conservation statute, California would be better prepared today to meet the test of war conditions. The people themselves, deliberately deluded by selfish and unscrupulous men, rejected the Oil Conservation Act which was passed by the California Legislature in the spring of 1939 and submitted to a referendum vote later that same year. I took a very real interest in this issue. The bill had the endorsement of the War and Navy Departments and of the President himself, but there were too many red herrings drawn across the trail by reckless and self-seeking individuals who had long thrived under the unregulated and disorganized conditions in the production of California oil and gas.

There was too much misrepresentation and there were too many falsehoods injected into the campaign for the proponents of the bill to overcome.

Because of the importance of California's oil in the war program, and in view of the lack of any state-sponsored regulation in the interest of conservation, the Petroleum Administration undertook, in cooperation with the production branch of the oil industry in California, a far-reaching conservation program designed to assure the production, at maximum operating efficiency and without waste of critical materials, of a continuing supply of California petroleum for war in the Pacific.

More recently, the special need for stimulating the discovery of additional crude reserves, particularly of the heavier grades of oil, has become apparent and we are endeavoring to encourage in every practical way the exploration, discovery, and development of California oil.

Another important oil-producing State that has no gas and oil conservation law is Illinois. The need for such a statute in that area is emphasized by the proximity of the Illinois petroleum reserves to the great war industries, military establishments, and centers of population in the Midwest.

Illinois' crude oil production, which averaged 370,-000 barrels daily in January 1942, has dropped to less than 250,000 barrels daily in recent weeks. This excessive decline in production, due to unsound practices, would not have occurred if an appropriate oil and gas conservation law had been in effect.

Although much of the waste already incurred in Illinois cannot now be remedied, the passage of remedial legislation at this time would prevent the continued, unwarranted waste of this valuable natural resource. With this in mind, the Petroleum Administration during the last session of the State legislature renewed its representations to the officials of Illinois that passage of a gas and oil conservation bill was imperative.

There is no immediate prospect that we will wake up some morning and find that all of our oil is gone out of the ground. But, over a period of years, we will be driven to obtain our supplies from more and more inaccessible deposits — deeper and more difficult and costly to find — and to employ increasingly elaborate methods of recovery.

Eventually oil will have to be imported, or distilled from oil shale or coal. These developments will be reflected in gradually rising prices with a corresponding loss of the benefits which now flow to the consumer as a result of wide distribution at low prices.

Germany, I am informed, has put approximately 1 million transported laborers to work on the construction of huge coal-oil plants in West Prussia and Silesia, and is said to be obtaining about one-third of its petroleum supply from coal resources.

The supply available to us from our own oil shale and coal will prove to be tremendous when the time comes that we have to resort to it.

As I have observed, we cannot maintain the 1943 rate of petroleum production without damage to the productive capacity of existing oil fields. This cannot be repeated too often. I have, therefore, urged that every feasible effort be made to increase the rate of discovery of additional reserves and to extract the last possible barrel from known fields. Moreover, I believe that the time is here when we should explore more seriously the possibilities of the recovery of oil from shale and by the hydrogenation of coal.

It is reliably estimated that there are in the western States and the black Devonian shales east of the Mississippi 92,000,000,000 barrels of extractable shale oil which would yield, upon cracking and refining, about 23 gallons of gasoline per barrel of shale oil. There are about 3,200 billion tons of coal in this country — enough solid carbonaceous material to produce synthetic liquid fuels at the rate of 1.5 billion barrels per year, plus 1 billion tons of coal per year for other fuel uses, for 1,000 years. On the other hand, a shortage of natural crude oil is by no means out of the bounds of possibility. Therefore, I believe that we should be making substantial progress in the study and actual production of crude oil from oil shale and from coal.

Through the work of the Bureau of Mines we have already had the benefit of 6 years of valuable laboratory experience, but funds to carry on have not been made available in recent years. Because of the great military importance of an adequate supply of indigenous liquid fuels, it would appear to me to be a wise national policy to build and to put into operation as quickly as possible at least one commercial pilot plant each for the production of oil from oil shale and from coal. These plants should not be built with the idea that they will be competitive with the oil industry, but rather that they will provide reliable data concerning the cost of production, the quality of products, and the time necessary to bring any desired capacity into production.

Such information would be made available to companies interested in the construction and operation of synthetic fuel plants, and might serve to encourage the conservation of our remaining natural gas and petroleum reserves. In this way the country would be placed in a position of security and preparedness in the development of adequate oil supplies for military and civilian purposes.

Strictly speaking, we are not so much under the urge to conserve the oil and gas that will be produced 20 and 30 years hence, although, despite present urgent preoccupations, we cannot afford to neglect this phase of the question for a minute. We are moved by the stern need to keep our daily productive capacity at the highest possible level for the next two, three, and four years, by which time we hope that the war will be over. At the moment, however, the war need is paramount and it requires, therefore, the relatively shorter view.

CHAPTER TEN

Still Another
War "Must"

No recital of our activities that disregarded the natural gas and natural gasoline resources of the Nation and their relation to the war program could be considered complete.

In addition to supplying the normal requirements of domestic, commercial, and industrial consumers, natural gas is a "must" in serving huge additional requirements of military installations.

The total consumption of natural gas for 1942 was approximately 3,000,000,000,000 (three trillion) cubic feet. This is equivalent in heating value to 600 million barrels of oil, or to 150 million tons of coal.

Natural gasoline and what are known as associated cycling plant products are needed primarily to obtain components used in increasing the output of vitally needed high-octane aviation gasoline. Special fractions of natural gas, natural gasoline, and cycling plant products are used as raw materials in plants manufacturing chemicals, explosives, and synthetic rubber. Many new and important uses are being discovered for these natural resources which make their contribution to the war program of tremendous importance.

The total production of natural gasoline and the associated cycling plant products for 1942 was in excess of 3.5 billion gallons.

In order to supply the increased demands, it has, of course, been necessary to increase production (where have I heard that expression before?) from existing facilities and to construct new facilities. This in turn has meant the drilling of new wells in proven areas and of exploratory wells to counterbalance the depletion suffered by producing fields. These wells are drilled to depths ranging from several hundred feet to almost three miles. As in the production of crude oil, it is important that the natural gas consumed be balanced by new discoveries as rapidly as possible in order to maintain supplies that will meet demands.

The problem in regard to our supply of natural gas is one that is not new to us. It is primarily a problem of having a sufficient amount of gas available for transportation to the place where it is to be used. Markets for gas have been developed in many sections of the country which are far removed from supply sources or where nearby sources now have been almost entirely exhausted. In the search for oil, many additional natural gas fields have been discovered until at the present time we have huge volumes of gas in reserve.

However, the rate of production of this gas is dependent upon the characteristics of the gas sand, or formation, and the mechanical equipment that is present. To increase the gas output from a field usually requires the drilling of additional wells, although in certain areas the wells already drilled will furnish more gas than the pipe lines are able to transport. In these instances, additional wells would be unnecessary until pipe-line capacities were increased.

In drilling to greater depths, unusual conditions have been encountered in natural gas and natural gasoline operations. Increased sand depth is, in general, accompanied by increased pressure and temperature. These factors have produced unusual conditions, heretofore believed impossible, by which heavier hydrocarbons generally found as liquids now exist in a reservoir in the " vapor state." Petroleum fractions existing in this so-called " vapor state " are referred to in trade circles as " condensates."

The processing of products found in condensate sands has resulted in the development and operation of the modern cycling plant. The cycling plant, after the processing of the natural gas for the removal of natural gasoline, cycles the dry gas back to the natural reservoir. The return of this product to the reservoir is of extreme importance, as pressure maintenance is a prerequisite to eliminating condensation and so preventing loss of the natural gasoline fractions due to the complex phenomenon which has been termed " retrograde condensation." The development of these so-called condensate fields has come at a most opportune time because the efficient methods by which natural gasoline is recovered from the reservoir, together with the minimum critical material requirements necessary for its production and processing, assure valuable additions to our ever increasing petroleum demand.

In normal times drilling, transportation, and extraction have been limited only by economic considerations. At this time, however, expansion is a military necessity.

In view of the critical shortage of steel, it is necessary to limit drilling in proven areas to the minimum needed for effective recovery, while at the same time we are encouraging drilling in promising areas. Similarly, it is necessary to limit transportation and extraction activities to the minimum needed to bring the available supply into balance with the existing demand.

The Natural Gas and Natural Gasoline Division of the Petroleum Administration for War has coordinated the activities relating to the production of these resources and, in the interest of assuring the most effective use of critical materials, has defined the conditions under which such materials may be used for drilling or for exploiting any well or for installing and operating any equipment.

An interesting problem arose in Southern California in connection with the storage of gas which, in that area, is usually produced in conjunction with crude oil. The nature of the oil business is such that the rate of crude production remains reasonably uniform throughout the year with a resultant even rate of production of natural gas. Natural gas companies purchase as much of this gas as their markets will absorb; however, the demand for it is much greater in winter than in summer. Thus, excess gas is produced in summer for which there is no use and which may have to be vented to the atmosphere for lack of storage facilities. This surplus gas represents a huge source of supply which, to be available when needed, and to avoid waste, must be stored.

A satisfactory reservoir for the storage of natural gas is a depleted oil or gas field. Some ten miles southwest of the city of Los Angeles is a depleted oil field known as the Playa del Rey. After careful surveys to establish the feasibility of underground storage at that point, authority was given for a project to inject natural gas under pressure to some 4,000 feet below the surface of the earth, and the necessary facilities are now under construction.

The reservoir will ultimately provide storage for 3 billion cubic feet of gas, of which 2 billion cubic feet will be withdrawn and replaced each year. The excess gas produced during the summer months will be transported to the storage field and compressed for injection into the sand. During the winter months this gas will be withdrawn to meet the increased requirements. The project will thus save a natural resource that would otherwise be wasted, will assist in providing a continuous supply of gas for fuel throughout the year for essential war uses in this area, and will use a minimum amount of critical construction materials to maintain the additional supply.

This is just one example of a storage project. There are many others using underground reservoirs for the storage of natural gas, located in various parts of the country.

Another very interesting method used for storing natural gas is now in operation in Cleveland, Ohio. This application is relatively new in practice but is proving very successful. It employs high pressure and a low temperature to liquefy natural gas. In the liquid state, the gas occupies only a fraction of its gaseous volume and therefore large quantities can be stored in a small space. It is stored in steel containers that are highly insulated to maintain a low temperature. In order to be used, however, the liquid must be converted back to its gaseous state. The special advantage of storage in this case is to have additional gas available near its point of consumption when pipe lines transporting gas from remote supply sources are carrying as much gas as they possibly can. This then amounts to an additional supply of gas available for use at any time that it is needed.

The natural gas industry is making a great contribution to the war program. Gas is a vital asset and the industry is being rapidly expanded to meet the increased military and war production demands with a minimum consumption of critical materials.

CHAPTER ELEVEN

Oil Across
the Sea

In one week not long ago the Foreign Division of the Petroleum Administration was engaged in working on oil problems affecting 38 countries! This may give some idea of the broad scope of our operations. (I mention it just in case someone has the idea that *all* of our troubles are on the home front.)

The Foreign Division's personnel includes men who speak almost any modern tongue — maybe some of the dead languages for all that I know to the contrary. There are men in the Department who know the Burma Road, the Pongo de Manseriche, the interior of China, and the headwaters of the Amazon.

If you walk into the offices of this particular branch of the Petroleum Administration, you can almost " hear " the rumble of the guns in Kasserine Pass or the hum of the bombers over the Bismarck Sea. For it is this Division that follows and checks the vast sources of supply that pump the life blood of war — gasoline — to all of the armies of the United Nations wherever they may be. There the long lines of supply upon which the various activities of the armed forces depend — the wells among the desert hills of the Persian Gulf, the refineries overlooking tropical seas, the terminals on remote coasts, and the tankers on the alert for submarines along the sea lanes — are watched.

Oil is a harvest which is reaped only if the seeds are planted long in advance. The bombs falling on Berlin today are carried there by gasoline which is the result of planning and work done two years ago. The supplies for the armies of 1945 must be planned in 1943 or even earlier.

This is not merely a question of drilling wells and building plants. It involves the geography of military operations. It requires a constant study of the future probabilities so that tankers and steel may be saved by producing oil for war requirements for any particular operation at the most favorable spot. This planning not only saves material, it also protects the lives of seamen who are subject to the constant danger of attack on the high seas.

At this point I wish to say that of all the brave men serving our country probably the most unsung are those who man the tankers carrying oil to our fighters. They are in momentary danger of death from an explosion, from fire, from drowning, from bombing. They get no medals for what they do. I stand in awe of a man who has the physical courage to face it without flinching.

In collaboration with the State Department, petroleum attachés have been sent to key countries throughout the world, and through them the Petroleum Administration is kept informed of the total petroleum requirements and of the materials that are necessary in the construction and development of the many projects under way. In fact, the Petroleum Administration works in close cooperation with the State Department, the Board of Economic Warfare and the Lend-Lease Administration concerning the many questions affecting petroleum supplies which arise with other Governments.

The Petroleum Administration, through its Foreign Division, acts as technical consultant in carrying out that part of the protocol with the Russian Government for refining plants and equipment for the Russian petroleum industry. It has supervision, also, over the actual delivery of petroleum supplies to Russia. For this work it has, of course, Russian-speaking personnel.

It consults with Brazilian authorities on the development of new oil fields in the Bahia area, and with Mexicans on the rehabilitation of their petroleum industry. It has assisted in the designing of special plants for China, and has aided in the selection of experts to go into the interior of that immense country to assist in exploring its little-known petroleum resources.

The Foreign Division works hand-in-glove with the Foreign Operations Committee of the petroleum industry organized by the Petroleum Administration, which is composed of representatives of most of the exporters and companies that operate abroad. This committee, in turn, has numerous related industry committees and subcommittees. Among the most important of these are the supply groups.

The first supply group organized was the Latin American Supply Committee which deals with the question of petroleum products that are carried by tankers to the Latin American markets. Its operations are based upon the principle of equity for all of the South American Republics. When there was an excess of tankers this was an easy problem, but with the increasing shortage of shipping facilities it has become necessary to reduce the amount shipped until by the middle of 1942 Latin American countries supplied by tankers were receiving for non-war purposes a basic allotment of only 40 per cent of their 1941 supply.

South American war industries, however, are furnished with petroleum products up to 100 per cent of their needs. The industries of Chile supplying copper and nitrate, those in Bolivia producing tin and tungsten, Brazilian companies furnishing black diamonds and iron ore (and I do mean " black diamonds " — industrial diamonds for cutting and abrasives, of which this country uses many millions of karats every year), the plants in the Guianas supplying aluminum, the sugar and alcohol refineries of the West Indies, get their full petroleum requirements. Their needs are passed upon by an Essential Requirements Committee composed of representatives of all of the government agencies concerned. The Latin American Supply Committee blueprints the requirements and sees that the supplies are available with tankers to transport them. It carries on its activities in cooperation with Pool Committees organized in the various countries which, in turn, keep the Supply Committee informed as to their needs. In most countries these Pool Committees are official government bodies subject to the control of the country in which they operate.

Besides the Latin American Supply Committee, there is a similar group operating for West Africa and one for the area between the Cape of Good Hope and Australia known as the Near East-Far East Supply Committee. These committees are in constant touch with the British supply groups so that the petroleum stocks for the entire world are coordinated between governments and industries. It should be pointed out here that in the countries which do not have crude oil production, rationing has been very strict. In such nations as Brazil, for example, private automobiles operate only in cases of emergency.

Industry Committees on production, refining, and transportation have also been organized, each of which has assembled data and made it available to the Petroleum Administration for use in its widespread activities.

Maps of terminals and plants are accessible to naval and military authorities for use in connection with their operations. Maps and data on producing oil fields, inventories, and distribution facilities enable the Petroleum Administration, through its Foreign

Division, to give, quickly and efficiently, a coordinated account of any particular area.

We have also interested ourselves in the question of standardization of products. In this field the Foreign Division and the technical divisions of the Petroleum Administration have worked closely with the Army and Navy and with the petroleum industry. To the average man the question of standardization seems a singularly abstruse subject. Boiling points, flash points, and viscosity indices seem remote from the practical affairs of field operations; nevertheless, they are of immense importance.

Modern war is fought with a vast array of complicated machines. To each machine must be brought the proper fuels and lubricants. At one time the air force of one of the United Nations required 126 varieties of lubricants. To supply so many different products in the right packages so that they could be readily identified at the front under battle conditions would fill our hospitals with quartermasters suffering from nervous breakdowns. This matter has, therefore, been under constant study, and the number of special products required is being steadily reduced, chiefly by the industry developing oils which will serve several specialized purposes.

When oil products are shipped we never know where they may go into service. Fuel oil must operate equally well in the heat of the Persian Gulf or in the icy seas of Murmansk. Lubricants must flow in the Russian winter in front of Novgorod or in the blistering winds of Alamein. Gasoline must start engines in the biting cold of Alaska (builders of the Alcan Road encountered 71° below zero weather last winter), and must not cause vapor lock in the steaming heats of the Burman coast. Ships leaving San Pedro may dock in Dutch Harbor, in the Aleutians, or halfway round the world at Guadalcanal.

Almost all products now going into foreign areas where our armed forces operate, whether for military purposes or not, are marked by symbols which indicate the uses to which they may be put, so that, if need be, the Army or Navy may use commercial stocks without fear of getting the wrong product for a particular service. Gasolines are dyed so that motor and aviation grades will not be mixed, nor will one grade of aviation fuel be taken for another. The oil industry has ceaselessly striven to develop new and more efficient products for the rigorous military services and, undoubtedly, one of the benefits that we will ultimately be able to salvage out of the maelstrom of war will be the improved performance of our oils and engines.

This work goes on constantly, not only with our own armed forces, but with representatives of other nations with which agreements are reached so that all of the military equipment employed by the Allies, with some small exceptions, now uses similar products for similar services.

Another group of specialists is studying the petroleum resources of the world with an eye to developing new production that would result in a saving in transportation. In such remote areas as China, New Zealand, Alaska, and the Persian Gulf, steps have already been taken to develop production, and, where oil has been found, to refine petroleum and petroleum products.

The Refining Section of the Foreign Division keeps a constant watch on refinery operations abroad. In ordinary times, currents of trade are well known and the volume requirements for certain products vary little from time to time. The reverse is true in wartime. While the demand for motor gasoline may go down, the demand for fuel oil of certain types may go up. High-octane gasoline, which was a rare commodity at the beginning of the war, has become one of the essential products and every effort is being made to produce it in great quantities. As a matter of fact, neither the armed forces nor the oil industry is now satisfied with 100-octane gasoline. We know now how to make gasoline of very much higher specifications. This will increase still further the maneuverability of our planes and make it possible for them to fly longer distances at higher rates of speed, carrying heavier loads of bombs.

The changes that I have discussed require shifts in refinery operations to eliminate bottlenecks and to prevent the accumulation of stocks of products not needed for the war.

Processes must be constantly adjusted — one day to produce more fuel oil for the Navy, and the next to obtain more 100-octane gasoline for the flying forces — while in the meantime production must be so balanced as between products that tanks do not overflow.

The industry has done a remarkable job abroad in adapting itself to these shifting conditions. For instance, a committee of refinery men in the Caribbean area has conferred from time to time for the purpose of improving the technical operations of plants, and with astonishing results. Despite the low demand for products that are normally produced, particularly heavy fuel oil, the production of 100-octane gasoline from existing facilities has been increased and the five great refineries in that area now operate as a unit for war purposes.

Another interesting activity of the Foreign Division is that which relates to the material used in the production, refining, and distribution of oil. The demands of foreign industry for such material are studied and checked by the Materials Section. When it is able to do so, this group suggests improvements in technique which result in a lower consumption of critical products. It also advises as to the preferential use of available materials. Its findings go to the War Production Board, and as a result allocations of material to the oil industry are set up so that the necessary production of oil and its refining and distribution can be carried on continuously abroad.

The Petroleum Administration works constantly, of course, with the armed forces. One of the special tasks that it performed was the compilation of lists of all of the men who have been drawn from the industry into the Army and who have operated abroad.

These lists have been useful to the Army in organizing groups to handle the petroleum problems of a military nature.

When the magnitude of this war is considered and full weight is attached to the fact that it extends to almost every section of the globe, it will be realized what a whale of a job the petroleum industry and the Government have done.

CHAPTER TWELVE

Oil in the Air

World War I gave impetus to the automotive industry, and for many years thereafter the keystone of our
national prosperity arch was the automobile. Closely
interrelated with it was the petroleum industry, which
had the profitable responsibility of pouring gasoline
into some 30 million automobiles and trucks.

Out of World War II another great industry —
aviation — will spring, and its closest ally, as in the
case of the automotive industry, will be petroleum.
There will never be 30 million airplanes (I hope) in
the air, but I believe that the flying business may surprise us by its growth and ultimate usefulness.

I realize that there are still a great many people who
shrug their shoulders when one suggests the possibilities (I would spell it distinctly " probabilities ") of

aviation. There are those who still believe that flying will never become practical, and I agree with them as against the one who expects it to take the place of all other forms of transportation. However, according to report, our grandfathers had an idea that Jules Verne was crazy, too, when, nearly a hundred years ago, he suggested the possibility of the submarine, the airplane, and of television.

Not so very long ago I happened to listen in on a radio program, the point of which was that, by 1946, we would be hearing airport announcers — and if my memory serves me correctly even they were women — crying the departure of express planes for Cairo and Moscow, and of " locals " for London. I am not quite ready to believe that within the short space of three years we will be hopping off for a week-end with friends in Russia, but I am not sure that the present generation won't be whisking through the air with as little thought as we now give to a motor ride to a roadhouse.

The close affinity that has existed between petroleum and aviation during the war should become an even closer and stronger bond when peace comes. To a greater degree even than with the automotive industry, aviation is a creature of petroleum. Conceivably, the automobile might have survived, after a fashion, without petroleum. It wouldn't, true enough, have developed 90 miles an hour on the open road, but with electricity, charcoal, and alcohol enough power might have been generated to have given it mobility if not speed. It would have been a little faster than some horses, perhaps; also noisier, and probably less dependable. No one knows.

Petroleum, on the other hand, is such an indispensable complement of the airplane that it stands to reason that without it there would have been no such thing as aviation and, as I have already had occasion to observe, a globe-encircling war would have been extremely unlikely.

Judged by present-day standards, it is difficult to think of World War I always in terms of a world war. At its outbreak the chief use of the airplane was in reconnoitering enemy positions and correcting military ranges. By the time Uncle Sam had landed his Army in France, the airplane was actually taking part in offensive undertakings, although compared to the modern armadas, the air squadrons of 25 years ago were definitely adolescent. This war *is* a world war in every sense of the word, and nothing but petroleum, plus aviation, has made it so.

I could name no branch of the armed service that is more popular with the youth of America than the air force. In fact, I don't think that anyone else could name one either. The air force has everything to attract the daring young man just as his forefathers were lured to the sea by the promise of swift-moving adventure in wide-open spaces. There is nothing in the cards to justify the opinion that our young men will lose their passion and instinct for flying as soon as they have dropped the last bombs on Berlin, Tokyo, and Rome. On the contrary, I expect to see them take to it in ever-increasing numbers. More than anything else except the telephone — speaking now of the personal touch — aviation is cutting down time and space, and in the business world of tomorrow this will be more of a factor than ever.

From the competitive standpoint, the United States should hold a strong advantage in the development of long-distance commercial air routes. Its experience and productive capacity alone warrant such a view. In this development the petroleum industry may be relied upon to play its usual important role. Both aviation and petroleum are young and glamorous industries, and in my mind's eye I can see them growing up together and leaning heavily the one upon the other. They are already inseparable and each is a part of the other. And although it is the fact that aviation is only one of petroleum's many important customers, it is equally true that aviation is growing fast and that it is going to grow faster in the post-war era. Petroleum has shown an amazing aptitude for keeping up with the times no matter how swiftly it " marches on." Remember how it measured steps with the automobile? And can we be so unappreciative as to forget how it has risen to the emergency of meeting the seemingly endless demands of the war?

Post-war problems of commercial aviation are even now engaging the attention of official Washington. A committee of six top-flight officials has been appointed and is at work to make a study upon which the national policy will be based. It has been well said that no question, not even excepting the Monroe Doctrine or America's 150-year-old advocacy of freedom of the seas, will transcend in importance the one concerning freedom of the air. Anyone who thinks of it as " globaloney " would make a goulash of the facts. The job of developing free trade, with free access to airports, subject only to quarantine, immigration, and traffic regulations, has already been undertaken, and it won't be long before it will come up for discussion in Congress. The opening and widening of air lanes in every direction is but one of the many things to be done when the war ends. The fact that serious thought is being given to it officially is an encouraging sign in itself.

The limiting factors in opening up the air lanes to every Tom, Dick, and Harry who owns or may own an airplane entail heavy responsibilities on those who must invent the regulations and attend to the policing of the blue serene. The laying down of rules under which a man in the air is to be permitted to run his noisy and dangerous machine without reference to the terrain beneath and the rights of those who dwell on it is a job that I would not want to find in my lap.

But if we needed anything to jolt us into accepting air travel as one of the coming dramatic means of going places, we had it in the President's historic flight to Africa. From Miami to Trinidad to Belém to Bathurst to Casablanca — four days from here to there — was something for anyone to do, to say nothing of a President of the United States. Considering that Grover Cleveland never went beyond the three-mile limit even to fish, we must admit that we have come a long way in our conceptions of time and space.

Returning, the President was on the hump of Brazil the morning after the night that he left Africa. He was in Trinidad the second day of travel and in Miami the next. The round trip measured nearly 17,000 miles, and it was negotiated in 10 days. The *net* traveling time furnishes an interesting commentary on air transportation. Most assuredly, the airplane is going to prove to be one of our most useful gadgets when this war is over. It will be helpful in advancing world trade, in promoting international good will, and, properly controlled, in protecting the world against even the possibility of World War III.

Consider the inevitable increase in passenger travel alone when it is again thrown open without restriction to a restless public that is suddenly released from the irksome " don'ts " of wartime. Men fresh out of the air force who aren't found in the drivers' seats of the peacetime planes, will be riding as passengers in the discharge of their civilian duties. No longer will the graduates, of that group at least, be satisfied with any slower mode of transportation.

Landing fields will be as common as baseball diamonds — and in most cases a great deal smoother and easier to land on. These will spot the countryside from shore to shore, their searchlights waving welcome to the traffic of the sky. Every urban community proudly will set aside a piece of ground within easy access of the center of its population where local planes and helicopters will fly in and out at all hours of the day and night with perhaps not quite the frequency of sparrows, but often enough at least to keep the air churning. The more prosperous members of the neighborhood will be going in for travel by helicopter just as they were the first to drive bright and shining

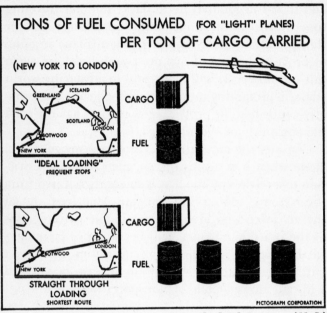

Courtesy " The Lamp," Standard Oil Company (N. J.)

limousines down Main Street to the amazement and envy of their townsmen.

I am not by any chance predicting the end of the usefulness of railroads and automobiles. Probably nothing will ever supplant them as common and private carriers. For all of the buses and the rapid advance of the automobile, both numerically and mechanically, the railroads now operate better, faster, and more comfortably run trains than ever. There will always be a rail-minded traveling public, just as there will always be a certain large percentage of people who will stick to the automobile for virtually all purposes, leaving a lesser segment that will never be weaned from ships to planes for ocean crossings.

Some are of the opinion that the giant passenger liner is a thing of the past. For some travelers nothing will ever take the place of the glorious days spent on board ship sniffing the salt air. Those who want to hurry may have their planes. I, personally, will stick to the more old-fashioned forms of travel.

Regardless of my preferences, I still think that the helicopter — or some other style of family aircraft — is a coming thing. One could spend a great deal of time, if he had it, dreaming about the possible uses of the helicopter. But your imagination is as good as mine, and I never did go in much for prophecy. (You will remember that at the very outset of this book I suggested that we might well afford to pay a fat fee to a major prophet to handle our oil problem. And I am not even a minor one.)

Much is expected of freight-carrying airplanes in the post-war era. Too much, possibly. Henry Kaiser thinks that he has the problem licked, at least in theory, and is experimenting on a small number of big transport planes. There are those who insist that we must master the ability to transport aerially goods by the many tons. Had it not been for Hitler's flying transports we would have had every Nazi in North Africa now occupying a grave, or a cubicle in a concentration camp, or swimming vainly in the direction of Sicily or Italy. So much for heavy transport to date in wartime.

The cargo planes of today, traveling long overwater routes, burn from one to four tons of fuel for every ton of freight carried. This fuel has to be carried to strategic points by tankers. On some routes cargo planes will need the services of as many tankers as they replace in freighters.

There are literally thousands of problems to be solved, each one giving rise to endless speculation. As we ponder them we are impressed by the tremendous possibilities that are wrapped up in these two great industries to challenge the imagination and the enterprise of future generations.

Petroleum! Aviation!

Two great doors swing wide open to the young people of today and tomorrow! I almost envy them!

APPENDIX

(AUTHOR'S NOTE: *The following letter, signed by 11 oil executives, was the means by which we proved back in 1941 that there were not " 20,000 idle railroad tank cars " available for use when our tanker service began to drop off. It is such a remarkable document that I believe its reproduction here will be of interest.*)

Washington, D. C.,
September 4, 1941.

Mr. Ralph K. Davies,
    Deputy Petroleum Coordinator
        for National Defense,
            Department of the Interior,
                Washington, D. C.

My dear Mr. Davies:

        Representatives of the following companies have met with you today to discuss the possibilities of special immediate action to increase the movement of petroleum products to the Atlantic Coast area:

    Gulf Oil Corporation
    Standard Oil Company of New Jersey
    The Texas Company
    Atlantic Refining Company
    Socony-Vacuum Oil Company
    Tidewater Associated Oil Company
    Cities Service Company
    Consolidated Oil Company

Sun Oil Company

American Oil Company

The Shell Oil Company

The transfer of tankers from usual operation on the Atlantic Coast we estimate decreased the tanker carrying capacity for the area by about 400,000 barrels daily. By special pipe line, barge, tank car and truck movement and increased efficiency, the industry has relieved the transportation deficiency so that stocks have been maintained at limits which have so far enabled the avoidance of hardship. The figures you have assembled based on statements obtained from the various individual companies indicate an estimated shortage averaging only 175,-000 barrels daily for the rest of the year if stocks are not heavily to be reduced and if no further tanker transfers occur. You will see therefore that very great progress has been made in minimizing the effect upon industry and the consuming public of the heavy withdrawal of tanker tonnage that has taken place.

You inform us it has been reported to you that there are an additional large number of tank cars available for use in transporting products to the area of shortage and you ask our intention with regard thereto. The answer is that we shall continue to press into service all available tank cars as rapidly as they can be supplied by the tank car companies and moved by the railroads and within, of course, the physical limitations as to trackage, unloading facilities, storage, etc. that exist. In view of the emergency we are prepared to vigorously prosecute this plan to the limit of the additional cars that are actually made available regardless of whether this proved to be

20,000, as you state is claimed by the railroads, or some other figure.

In an endeavor to move as rapidly as possible and pending the working out of more complete recommendations for equitable participation by the entire industry through the industry committees now functioning, these companies are prepared to do the following in addition to the many steps heretofore taken:

1. Each company will immediately ask for and utilize in petroleum transportation all the available railroad tank cars it can obtain to the extent that its storage, car loading, other facilities and requirements will permit until shortage conditions are terminated.

2. Each company will at once endeavor to increase its loading and unloading facilities to the extent necessary to utilize its full storage capacity.

3. The increased costs per barrel of petroleum products by tank car transportation over the Maritime Commission charter rate ceilings for tankers will be shared equitably by the signatory companies under a plan to be developed and recommended by the Transportation Committee of District No. 1 and approved by the Petroleum Coordinator.

It is obvious that mass movement of crude oil and products by tank car, as against the normal shipment by tanker, must result in a very substantial increase in transportation costs and it is hoped that the applications we have so far made and those which we shall make hereafter for reduced railway rates will be promptly approved by the railroads, thus obviating the necessity for placing upon the buying public the full burden of this emergency expense. It impresses us as being only fair that the railroads should, in these circumstances, make some substantial contribution.

The companies will not ask for the sanction of any price increase on account of increased transportation costs until appropriate showing has been made in justification thereof. However, in view of the greatly increased transportation cost which must inevitably result from movement by tank car in lieu of movement by the usual tanker method, it is our expectation that when required to make some price adjustment as a reasonable offset to the added and abnormal expense, that our application will have fair consideration by the Office of Price Administration. Further, it is our understanding that your office will support with Mr. Henderson such applications for equitable adjustment.

Sincerely yours,

Gulf Oil Corporation

Standard Oil Company of New Jersey

The Texas Company

Atlantic Refining Company

Socony- Vacuum Oil Company

Tidewater Associated Oil Company

[signature] Vice President

Cities Service Company

[signature]

Consolidated Oil Company

[signature]

Sun Oil Company

[signature: J. Howard Pew]

American Oil Company

[signature: Robert E. Wilson]

The Shell Oil Company

[signature]

(AUTHOR'S NOTE: *Some of the terms listed here are used in the book. Others are not. All of them are commonly used in the petroleum language. They are included in the hope that they may throw additional light on the Story of Oil.*)

ALKYLATE   A type of synthetic blending agent used in the manufacture of aviation gasoline to produce high anti-knock and low vapor pressure characteristics in the finished blend. It is manufactured by combining certain refinery or natural gases in the presence of a catalyst.

ALLOCATION   The distribution of production quotas to wells and pools for the purpose of accomplishing ratable and equitable withdrawals from the reservoir and to prevent the waste of oil and reservoir energy.

ALLOWABLE   Crude oil production rate at which a well, lease, pool or field is permitted to produce under proration. Usually measured in barrels per day.

AROMATIC   A group of hydrocarbon compounds used to augment the rich mixture performance of aviation gasoline. Aromatic blending agents are produced by various refinery processes, and also as by-products of coal tar distillation. Those now in use are benzene, toluene, xylene, and cumene.

ASPHALT   Solid or semi-solid native bitumen. Also obtained by refining petroleum or solid or semi-solid bitumen.

AVIATION GASOLINE   Actually not gasoline at all, but a superfuel produced by rearranging the petroleum hydrocarbon molecules through the use of catalysts. The requirements that are significant in aviation gasoline are high anti-knock characteristics, low vapor pressure, satisfactory volatility, and high rich mixture performance. It has not thus far been possible to develop in commercial production a single component possessing all of these properties in the desired degree. Consequently, it is necessary to produce this superfuel through appropriate blending of the different components, each of which possesses one or more of the above properties.

BARREL   One barrel of oil equals 42 gallons U.S.A., or 35 British Imperial gallons.

BASE STOCK   As used in relation to aviation gasoline, base stocks are the volume ingredients into which the blending agents are introduced. The higher the anti-knock value of the base stock the greater the amount of finished aviation gasoline from a given amount of blending agent.

BLENDING   Adding one oil to another so that the mixture is homogeneous in all its parts.

BOTTOM HOLE PRESSURE   Pressure at or near the bottom of an oil well, or any well which produces a fluid, usually determined by means of a recording instrument which is lowered into the well.

BUNA RUBBER   A rubberlike material made from synthetic materials. Of all the synthetic rubberlike
materials, the Buna group most closely resemble
natural rubber, and are the type making up most
of the capacity being installed in the United
States.

BUTADIENE   A pure chemical, made from petroleum
or grain alcohol. It is the most important constituent of Buna rubbers.

BUTYLENES   Light unsaturated hydrocarbons produced by " cracking " butane or other petroleum
hydrocarbons. One of the butylenes — isobuty-
lene — is the base of butyl rubber. Others of the
butylenes — normal butylenes — are used as raw
materials for the production of butadiene. Any
or all of the butylenes can be polymerized with
isobutane to produce " alkylate " blending agents
for aviation gasoline.

BUTYL RUBBER   A rubberlike material made from
refinery gases. It is comparatively simple to manufacture but is inferior in most applications to
Buna or natural rubbers.

CATALYST   Any substance which, solely by its presence, initiates or accelerates chemical reaction between two or more other chemicals.

CATALYTIC CRACKING   Splitting, or reforming petroleum into a number of new and lighter hydrocarbon compounds in the presence of a catalyst.
Catalytic cracking of petroleum to get high-grade
synthetic engine fuels is a relatively new basic
technique in gasoline refining. Various processes

may be employed but they are alike in their basic purpose which is to effect greater internal change in petroleum's natural structure — to take it apart in more detail — to put the parts together again with more precision — than has ever before been possible.

CHRISTMAS TREE   Surface installation of valves and fittings at the top of a flowing well. So called because of the numerous gadgets attached thereto.

COLLOIDAL FUEL   A combination of fuel oil and finely powdered coal which remains in suspension.

CONDENSATE FIELD   A field from which both gas and liquid hydrocarbons are produced, both of which existed as a " single phase " under the original reservoir condition. So called because the liquid hydrocarbons " condense out " when the pressure and temperature are lowered.

CUMENE   A high anti-knock, aromatic blending agent used to improve rich mixture characteristics of superfuel.

DIESEL OIL   A fuel oil which is suitable for use by Diesel oil engines. The oil must be clean, containing neither water nor solid matter.

DISTILLATE   Any condensed product of distillation.

DRY HOLE   Any well that does not result in the discovery of oil or gas in commercial quantities.

DRY NATURAL GAS   A gas that does not contain any considerable amount of easily separated gasoline.

FLUID CATALYTIC PROCESS   One of the principal processes referred to under CATALYTIC CRACKING above.

FRACTIONATION   A process of separating a mixture of hydrocarbons into one or more constituent compounds, or groups of compounds.

FUEL OIL   Any product of petroleum, from which naphtha and other light fractions have been removed, used to produce power or heat. Fuel oils range from heavy or residual fuel oils to light or distillate fuel oils.

GAS OIL   A petroleum oil of medium gravity which is used for enriching water gas to increase its luminosity, or is used as a high-grade fuel oil; also a raw material used in cracking processes.

GAS OIL RATIO   The relative volume of gas that is produced with crude oil in the production operation. Natural gas, stored with and dissolved in the oil under pressure, provides the " reservoir energy " which drives the oil through the sand to the well and forces the oil to rise to the surface of the ground in the case of a " flowing well," which produces without pumping. It is essential that the minimum possible volume of gas be produced with the oil in order to conserve the gas energy in the producing formation. In cases of so-called " water drive " fields, the reservoir energy is supplied by the pressure of water beneath the oil, forcing it through the sands to the well.

GASOLINE, SYNTHETIC   Artificial gasoline from substances other than petroleum or its products.

HOUDRY PROCESS   A catalytic process — one of the

principal processes referred to under CATALYTIC CRACKING above.

HYDROCARBON   A compound containing only a combination of carbon with hydrogen.

HYDROGENATION   A process of converting hydrocarbons to other hydrocarbons by causing hydrogen to combine with the raw materials, usually in the presence of a catalyst.

ISO-OCTANE   The name of a specific hydrocarbon of the gasoline family. Iso-octane, like alkylate, is one of the principal synthetic blending agents used in the manufacture of aviation gasoline.

KNOCK   The name given to the sharp pinging noise which gasoline engines produce when the engine is consuming a gasoline having a lower octane number than that which it is adjusted to burn.

LIGNITE   A brownish-black coal in which the alteration of vegetal material has proceeded further than in peat but not so far as in sub-bituminous coal.

MARGINAL WELL   A small well of settled production. The term refers to the economic position of a well and not to its location.

NATURAL GAS   A hydrocarbon gas of variable composition that may or may not be associated directly with petroleum.

NATURAL GASOLINE   A product from wet gas of an oil-bearing reservoir. Sometimes referred to as "casinghead gasoline." Natural gasoline is used in the manufacture of motor fuel and is playing an important role in the aviation gasoline program.

OCTANE NUMBER (O.N.)   A term used to describe the potential performance of gasoline; it measures the detonating property of the motor fuel. Numerically, it is the percentage of iso-octane (very high-grade motor fuel) in heptane (very low-grade motor fuel) which gives performance equivalent to the fuel under test.

OIL RESERVOIR   The portion of the earth in which oil has been entrapped. Usually known as a pool.

OIL SHALE   A bituminous shale which is heated to decompose the bituminous matter and produce hydrocarbon oils.

OIL STRUCTURE   Underground condition in the rock formation, such as a dome or anticline, which has resulted in the entrapping of oil.

POLYMERIZATION   A process by which hydrocarbon gases may be converted to heavier hydrocarbon compounds, such as gasoline.

POTENTIAL   Maximum short-time capacity at which a well, lease, pool, or field can produce. Usually measured in barrels per day.

PRODUCING HORIZON OR ZONE   The underground layer of rock, usually sand or porous limestone, in which oil or gas has been trapped and from which the oil or gas is now being produced.

PRORATION   Distribution of production quota of a pool or state among the wells or pools therein. Often used to designate the curtailment of a well, lease, pool, or field production rate to an amount less than capacity production. This practice has been followed by state regulatory bodies to restrict production to efficient rates in order to prevent physical waste or to allocate crude oil requirements equitably among wells, leases, pools, or fields.

RICH MIXTURE RATING A special type of rating designed to measure the potential performance of aviation gasoline during take off or other occasions when peak power is required.

SALT WATER WELLS Wells producing only salt water.

SCREENING A reviewing process whereby applications for critical materials are studied and those that are considered unessential to the war program or wasteful in the use of materials are weeded out.

SECONDARY RECOVERY The recovery of crude oil from an underground reservoir by means of injecting gas, air or water into the reservoir after it has been largely depleted, thereby driving additional oil to the producing wells and effecting increased recovery.

STRIPPER WELL A small well in the last stages of production, yielding only enough oil barely to justify its continued operation.

SYNTHETIC RUBBER A group of rubberlike materials which are built up from hydrocarbons and accessory compounds, all or nearly all of which are of synthetic origin. Synthetic rubber is superior to or inferior to natural rubber, depending upon the use for which it is designed and the compounding employed.

THERMOFOR PROCESS   One of the principal processes referred to under CATALYTIC CRACKING above.

TOLUENE   A pure chemical obtained from coal tar and petroleum. It is used to make TNT explosive, and is also one of the aromatic blending agents used in the manufacture of aviation gasoline.

TON   A ton of gasoline measures between 8 and $8\frac{1}{2}$ barrels of 42 gallons each. For heavier grades of oil the number of barrels in a ton would be less.

THROUGHPUT   A colloquialism that describes the amount of oil that is put through a refinery each day.

VISCOSITY   The property of an oil or other liquid that determines its rate of flow — the measure of the degree of its fluidity.

WATER FLOODING   A secondary recovery operation whereby water is injected into the reservoir to drive the oil to the producing wells.

WET NATURAL GAS   Natural gas which contains readily extractable " natural gasoline."

WILDCAT   A well in an unproved territory. Analogous to " prospect " in mining, rather than to a wildcat financial enterprise. A more specific definition has been required for inclusion in Petroleum Administration orders.

TYPE NOTE

The text of this book has been set on the Linotype in a type-face called " Baskerville." The face is a facsimile reproduction of types cast from molds made for John Baskerville (1706–1775) from his designs. The punches for the revived Linotype Baskerville were cut under the supervision of the English printer George W. Jones. John Baskerville's original face was one of the forerunners of the type-style known as " modern face " to printers: a " modern " of the period A.D. 1800.

The typography of this book was planned by S. R. Jacobs and W. A. Dwiggins. The binding was designed by W. A. Dwiggins. The book was composed, printed, and bound by The Plimpton Press, Norwood, Massachusetts.